STAR WARS

GALACTIC ADVENTURES

DISNEY

LUCASFILM
PRESS

Los Angeles • New York

"Escape from Darth Vader" written by Brooke Dworkin and illustrated by Stephane Roux.
"The Battle of Hoth" written by Calliope Glass and illustrated by Pilot Studio.
"Rescue from Jabba's Palace" written by Brooke Dworkin and illustrated by Pilot Studio.
"Destroy the Death Star" written by Trey King and illustrated by Pilot Studio.
"A Jedi, You Must Become" written by Andy Schmidt and illustrated by Stephane Roux and Pilot Studio.
"The Ewoks Join the Fight" written by Brooke Dworkin and illustrated by Pilot Studio.

A long time ago in a galaxy far, far away. . . .

ESCAPE FROM DARTH VADER

IT WAS a time of war. Rebel spies fought the sinister Empire for control of the galaxy.

One of the rebels was named Princess Leia. She had been given plans for the Empire's newest weapon—the Death Star. Destroying the weapon before it could be activated was the rebels' only hope to defeat the Empire. But that meant getting the plans back to the rebel base.

Now Leia was on her starship, heading home to Alderaan to share the plans with the other rebels. But she was not alone. An Imperial ship was chasing her!

On board Leia's ship, a tall golden droid named C-3PO grew worried.

"We're doomed," he said to his short blue-and-silver companion, R2-D2. "There'll be no escape for the princess this time!"

C-3PO was right. A loud explosion rocked the ship. It had been captured!
As the droids watched, the starship's main door blasted open. Stormtroopers rushed through, swarming the ship.

The rebels fired their blasters at the attackers, but they were no match for the Imperial stormtroopers. One by one the rebels fell. Soon the stormtroopers were in full control of the ship.

R2-D2 beeped at C-3PO urgently. They had to get away before it was too late.

As the two droids escaped, a mysterious figure emerged from the smoke. He wore a long cloak, and his body was covered with black armor. It was Darth Vader, a dark and powerful Sith Lord.

Darth Vader's mechanical breathing echoed through the halls. Now that he had captured the starship, it was only a matter of time before he recovered the stolen plans.

In the confusion, C-3PO lost sight of R2-D2.

C-3PO looked everywhere for his friend. "Artoo-Detoo, where are you?" he called.

Elsewhere on the ship, Princess Leia looked at the plans for the Death Star. She knew she had to keep them safe. If the Empire got the plans back, the rebels wouldn't stand a chance!

Just then, R2-D2 appeared. Seeing the droid gave Princess Leia an idea.

Princess Leia leaned over and began speaking to the droid. She was recording a message for someone she hoped could help her and the Rebel Alliance.

"I have placed information vital to the survival of the Rebellion into the memory systems of this Artoo unit," she explained.

Then Leia inserted the plans for the Death Star into R2-D2 and told the droid where to go.

Princess Leia finished her instructions and quickly hid so Darth Vader wouldn't find her.

Just then, C-3PO spotted R2-D2. "At last!" he said. "Where have you been?"

Before the little droid could answer, they heard stormtroopers approaching. "They're heading in this direction," C-3PO said. "What are we going to do?"

But R2-D2 wasn't listening. He turned around and zipped off down the corridor.

Princess Leia waited until she was sure R2-D2 was safe. Then, lifting her hood over her head, she crept through the shadows. There was still a chance she could get away, too!

Meanwhile, Darth Vader and his troops stood before the captured crew.

"The Death Star plans are not in the main computer," an Imperial commander reported.

That did not make Darth Vader happy. "Tear this ship apart until you've found those plans," he ordered. "And bring me the passengers!"

It turned out that the Death
Star plans—and R2-D2—were
about to leave the ship. The
little astromech droid and
C-3PO were heading toward
an escape pod.

"You're not permitted
in there," C-3PO said. "It is
restricted. You'll be
deactivated for sure!"

R2-D2 beeped back at him.

"Secret mission?" C-3PO
asked. "What plans? I'm not
getting in there!"

Just then, another explosion
rocked the ship.

C-3PO hurried into the pod.
"I'm going to regret this," he
said.

The door slammed, and the
escape pod rocketed off into
space.

A short while later, the pod landed on a desert planet named Tatooine.

The droids stepped out onto the sand.

"How did we get into this mess?" C-3PO asked. There was nothing and no one around for miles!

The plans were safe, but the droids' adventures were just beginning. They were the Rebel Alliance's only hope to stop Darth Vader.

DESTROY THE DEATH STAR

FOR YEARS the Rebel Alliance had struggled against Darth Vader and the evil Galactic Empire. Now, for the first time, the rebels had an advantage. Thanks to Princess Leia and her faithful droids, R2-D2 and C-3PO, the Rebellion had been able to study the Empire's greatest weapon—the Death Star. And they had found a weakness!

As Luke Skywalker prepared for the attack on the Death Star, he turned to his friend Han Solo. "They could use a good pilot like you," he said.

"Sorry, kid," Han said. He was a smuggler. He had more important things to do.

Luke walked away. He was disappointed, but he needed to keep his mind on the mission. At times like this, he missed his old teacher, the Jedi Master Obi-Wan Kenobi.

Luke climbed into the cockpit of his X-wing while they loaded his astromech droid, R2-D2, into the ship. Luke was glad to have the little droid as his copilot. The two friends had been through a lot together.

The fleet of X-wing fighters took off toward the Imperial space station.

"Look at the size of that thing," one of the pilots said.

As they approached the massive Death Star, everyone started to get nervous.

Then Luke heard a voice inside his head: *Luke, the Force will be with you....* It was Obi-Wan!

Soon the Death Star's cannons began to shoot at the X-wings. Laser fire exploded all around Luke and his friends. Luckily, the X-wings had been designed to move with speed and agility. There was no time for hesitation.

"I'm going in," Luke said, dodging the attack.

Luke heard the voice again: *Luke, trust your feelings.*

Obi-Wan's voice helped Luke focus on the battle. He avoided the enemy laser fire and swooped toward the surface of the Death Star with the other X-wings.

But the X-wings were not alone. A fleet of TIE fighters appeared behind them. That was going to make things even more difficult—especially since Darth Vader himself was leading the enemy ships.

The TIE fighters fired on the X-wings. Luke's ship was shot!

"I'm hit, but not bad," Luke told the other pilots. "Artoo, see what you can do back there."

The little droid quickly went to work on repairs as Luke dodged another fighter.

The first of the X-wings entered a trench in the Death Star. The lead pilot got close to the exhaust port—the one weakness of the giant space station.

The pilot fired . . . but he missed!

Back at the rebel base, Princess Leia and C-3PO were worried about their friends. But they were also worried about the Death Star. If it got too close to their base, it would destroy them all!

The second attack run of rebel ships dove into the canyon to take their shot. But they missed, too! Now it was all up to Luke. He just had to dodge Darth Vader and the enemy TIE fighters on his tail.

Luke was almost in range. He tried to use the targeting computer to make the shot. Then he heard Obi-Wan's voice again: *Use the Force, Luke.*

Luke shut off the computer. He needed to trust himself. Just as Luke was about to take the shot, Darth Vader's TIE fighter appeared behind him. The Imperial leader locked on to Luke's X-wing.

"I have you now," Vader said triumphantly.

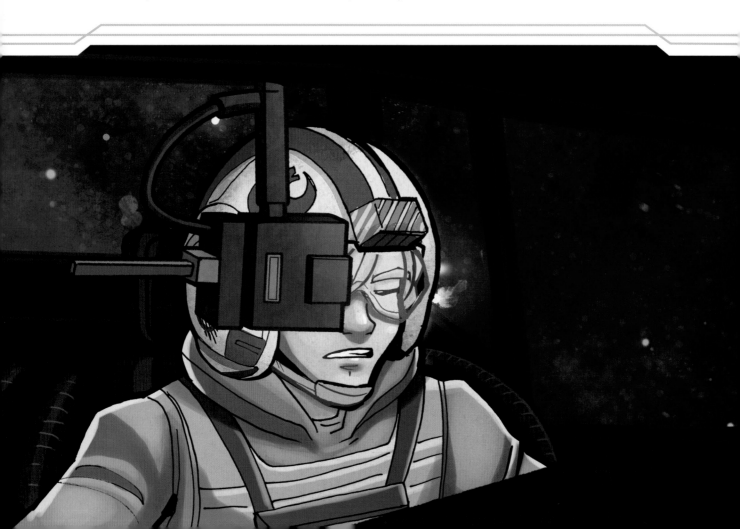

But before Darth Vader could fire, another ship swooped in and rocked his TIE fighter with a cannon blast. It was Han Solo in the *Millennium Falcon*! He had returned just in time to save his friends.

"Yahoo!" Han cheered as he took out two of the TIE fighters. His next blast sent Darth Vader's ship spiraling away into space. "You're all clear now, kid," Han said to Luke. "Now let's blow this thing and go home!"

Luke was happy his friend had joined the fight after all.

But everything still rested on Luke's shoulders. If he didn't make the shot, the rebels were doomed. Luke thought about what Obi-Wan had said.

He closed his eyes and felt the Force flow through him. He waited. Then, when the moment was right, he fired.

The torpedoes flew into the exhaust port of the Death Star.

"Great shot, kid!" Han Solo said. "That was one in a million!"

The rebel ships sped away from the Death Star as fast as they could.

Seconds later, the entire space station exploded in a giant burst of light! The Death Star had been destroyed.

As Luke and his friends flew to safety, Luke heard Obi-Wan's voice in his head once again. *Remember, the Force will be with you. Always.*

Luke smiled to himself. He and his friends had destroyed the Death Star and protected the rebel base. Soon they would save the entire galaxy.

THE BATTLE OF HOTH

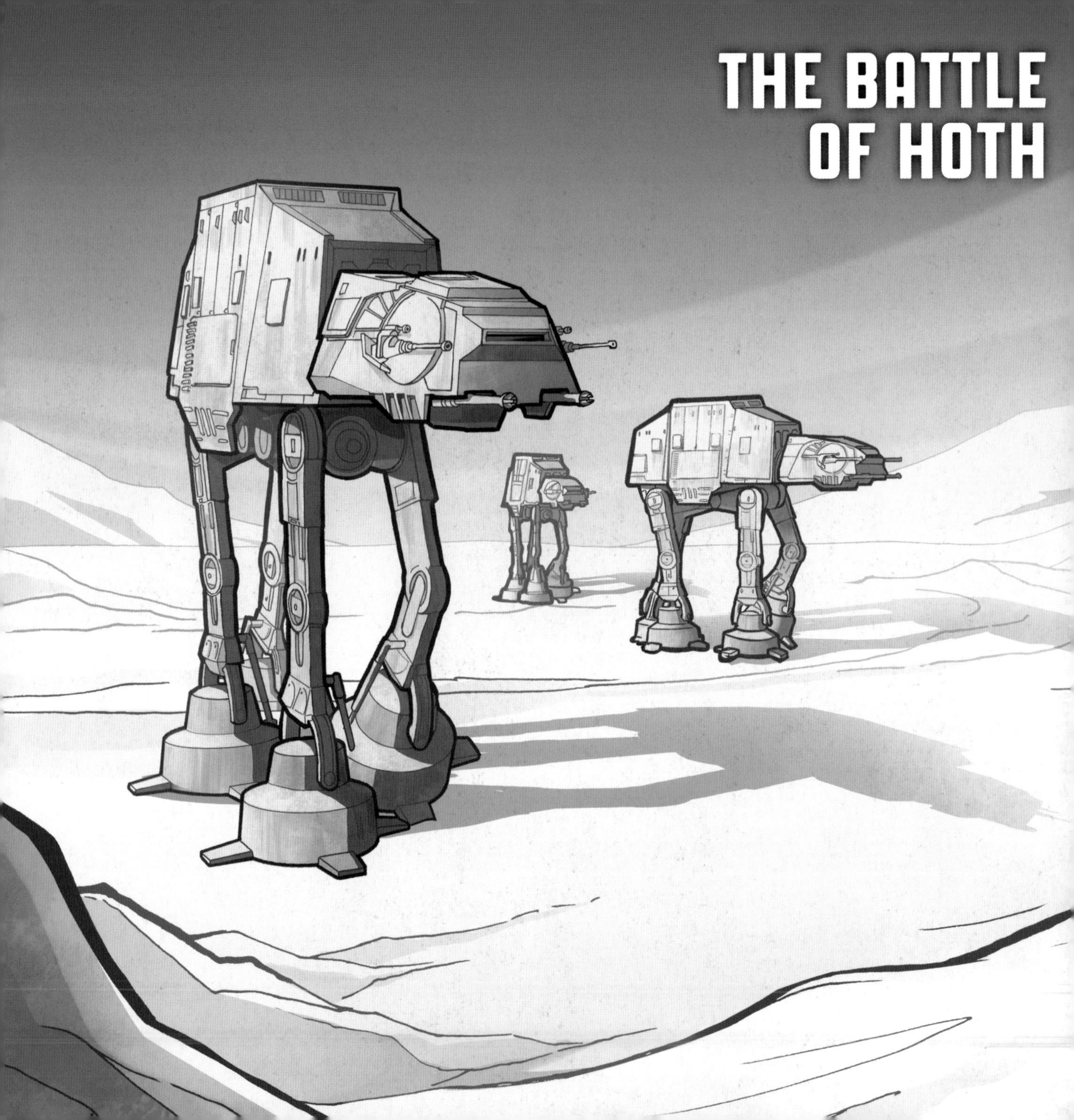

DEEP IN the cold reaches of space, the ice planet Hoth orbited a pale sun. The surface of the planet was a frozen wasteland. Nobody lived there. At least, nobody was *supposed* to live there. That made Hoth the perfect place for the Rebel Alliance to hide from the evil Empire.

   Although the Death Star had been destroyed, the Empire's troops, led by Darth Vader, were still very powerful.

Vader was looking everywhere for the Rebel Alliance. He had sent hundreds of probe droids into space, seeking any sign of the rebels.

One day the rebels noticed a droid snooping around their base on Hoth.

"Come on, Chewie," Han Solo told his Wookiee copilot. "Let's check it out."

The droid self-destructed before Han could get to it. But it had already sent a signal to Darth Vader. The secret rebel base wasn't a secret anymore.

Darth Vader wasted no time. His fleet left for the Hoth system right away.

Soon four armored Imperial walkers began to make their way across the icy tundra toward the rebel base. Princess Leia ordered everyone to evacuate. Most of the rebels hurried onto transport ships and left immediately. But others, including Leia and Han, remained behind to protect the base.

Meanwhile, Luke Skywalker led a squadron of fighter pilots in snowspeeders onto the plains of Hoth. They were going to try to fend off the monstrous Imperial walkers. Luke hoped his squadron would be able to keep the walkers far away from the base…and far away from his friends Leia and Han.

Luke's squadron tried firing directly at the walkers, but it did no good. "That armor's too strong for blasters," Luke declared. He came up with a new plan. He used a cable instead, tangling one of the walker's legs together.

It worked! But the rebel fighters were still outnumbered.

Luke ejected from his snowspeeder and ran beneath a walker. He fired a grappling hook and pulled himself up to its belly. Then he used his lightsaber to cut it open.

He threw a grenade into the walker and dropped back to the ground. *Boom!* The walker flashed with green sparks and exploded.

Even as Luke tried to keep the walkers away, the rebel base was taking fire. The floor shook violently. Han and Leia could barely stand up! Then the alert came: "Imperial troops have entered the base."

Han grabbed Leia's hand. "Come on," he said. It was time to go.

Han led Leia toward his ship, the *Millennium Falcon*. The golden droid C-3PO followed on their heels.

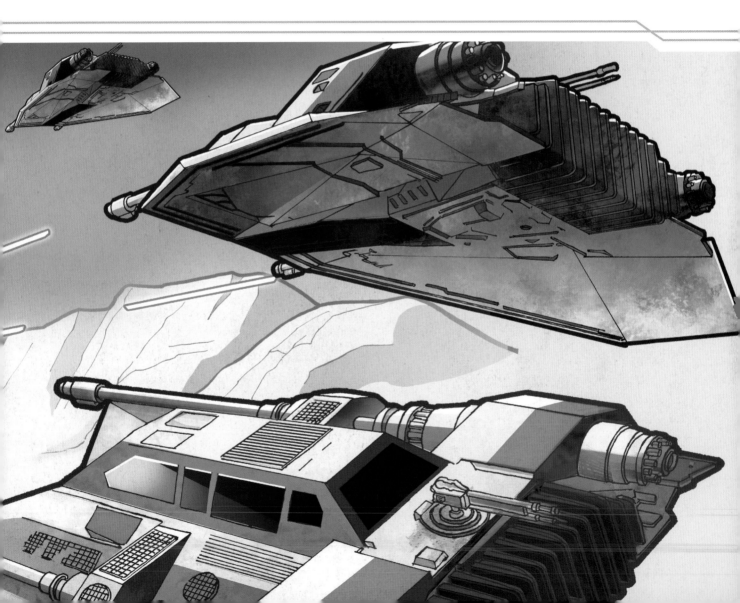

Darth Vader personally led his Imperial troops into the rebel base. As the troops searched for any remaining rebels, Chewie and Han tried to get the *Millennium Falcon* started. The engine revved, then choked. Steam billowed everywhere.

"Would it help if I got out and pushed?" Leia asked sarcastically.

"It might!" Han snapped.

Han and Chewie worked furiously to get the ship running. Leia was worried. They were going to be captured by the Empire unless they could get the *Millennium Falcon's* engine started.

Just as Han and Chewie were making their final repairs, Darth Vader led a group of Imperial snowtroopers into the hangar where the *Millennium Falcon* was docked. They opened fire on the ship.

The ship's engine rumbled to life as Han and Chewie returned fire.

"See?" Han said to Leia.

The princess rolled her eyes.

"Someday you're going to be wrong," Leia told Han as the ship leapt into the air and rocketed out of the base. "I just hope I'm there to see it."

Darth Vader watched angrily as the ship escaped into the sky.

A short distance away, Luke Skywalker watched them go. The *Millennium Falcon* was the last ship to leave the base. Luke had done his job, and Han and Leia had gotten away.

The Rebel Alliance was safe. Luke could not do any more for them at the moment. Now, he had his own mission to complete.

A JEDI, YOU
MUST BECOME

LUKE SKYWALKER had always been brave. He had fought heroically against the evil Empire as a pilot for the Rebel Alliance. He had even destroyed the enormous Death Star!

But being brave didn't make him a Jedi. Luke decided that he could best help the rebels if he became a Jedi Knight—and for that he needed special training.

Luke's old friend Obi-Wan Kenobi had appeared to him in a vision. *You will go to the Dagobah system,* he had said. *There you will learn from Yoda, the Jedi Master who instructed me.*

Obi-Wan's words echoed in Luke's head. He knew the message was very important. He called his droid, R2-D2, and they set a course for Dagobah.

As Luke turned his X-wing toward the planet, he checked his radar. "I'm not picking up any cities or technology. Massive life-form readings, though. There's something alive down there. . . ."

Suddenly, Luke's ship lost power. He tried to land the X-wing, but it was out of control. The ship crashed into a giant swamp.

Climbing out of the X-wing, Luke and R2-D2 waded to shore. Dagobah was not what Luke had expected. He thought a Jedi Master would live on a refined planet with gorgeous landscapes—but that was not what Dagobah was like at all!

The planet was wet, muggy, and crawling with bugs, critters, and wild animals. It could be summed up with one word—*gross*!

Suddenly, Luke felt someone watching him. He spun around, pulling out his blaster. Standing in front of Luke was a pale green creature with big pointy ears.

"Away put your weapon," the creature said. "I mean you no harm."

Luke doubted very much that the strange little creature could help him, but he explained, "I'm looking for a Jedi Master."

"Ohhhhh. Jedi Master," the creature replied. "Yoda. You seek Yoda. Take you to him I will."

Luke followed the creature in search of Yoda, but instead they ended up at a small mud hut, where the creature offered Luke some dinner.

Luke grew impatient. "We're wasting our time!" he said loudly.

The creature turned away from Luke. "I cannot teach him," he said quietly. "The boy has no patience. . . . He is not ready."

He will learn patience, replied a voice—Obi-Wan Kenobi's voice!

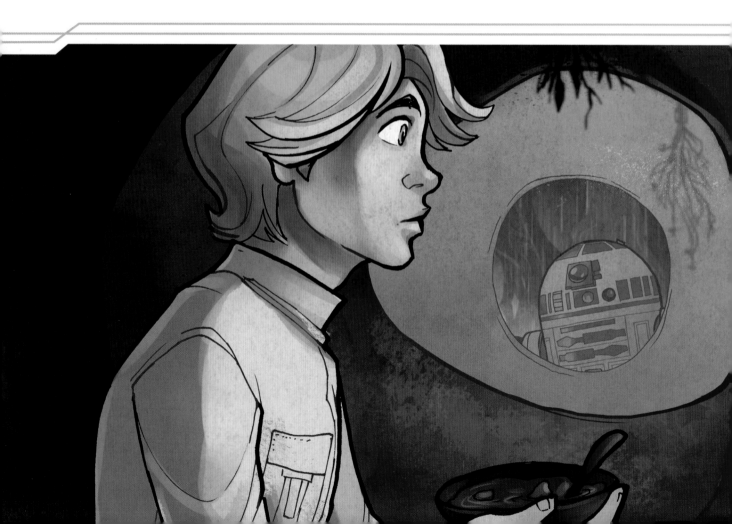

Luke suddenly realized that this was no ordinary creature. "Yoda!" he cried.

But Yoda looked at Luke sternly. "Adventure—ha! Excitement—ha! A Jedi craves not these things. You are reckless."

Luke pleaded with Yoda. He told him he was not afraid and he was ready to learn.

Finally, Yoda agreed to train him.

As Luke trained his body, Yoda helped him develop his mind.

"A Jedi uses the Force for knowledge and defense," Yoda said, "never for attack."

Luke began to understand that being a Jedi was less about him and more about helping others.

Luke also learned to use the Force to move objects. One day, Luke stacked a whole tower of rocks just by concentrating on the Force—while standing on his head! But as he was placing the final rock, he saw his X-wing sinking deeper into the swamp. Luke lost his concentration and fell to the ground with a thud.

Yoda told Luke to use the Force to raise his ship out of the bog.

"Moving stones around is one thing," Luke replied, "but this is totally different."

"No, no different," Yoda said. "You must unlearn what you have learned."

Luke concentrated. He knew that he would one day have to confront Darth Vader. He needed to be as strong in the Force as possible.

Luke turned back to the sunken X-wing. "All right," he said, "I'll give it a try. . . ."

Yoda corrected Luke. "Do. Or do not," he said. "There is no try."

Luke focused on Yoda's words, letting the Force flow through him.

Slowly, the X-wing began to rise! Luke watched it in wonder and surprise. The little droid R2-D2 beeped and whistled in excitement.

But Luke still felt doubt. He knew that an X-wing was very heavy. How could be possibly manage to lift it? Slowly, the ship sank back into the swamp.

Luke was discouraged. "I can't. It's too big."

"Size matters not," Yoda said. "Look at me. Judge me by my size, do you?"

Yoda reached out with his tiny old hand, and the ship began to move!

Yoda concentrated even more and the ship floated through the air until it came to rest on solid ground.

"I don't believe it," Luke said, astonished.

"That," Yoda replied, "is why you fail."

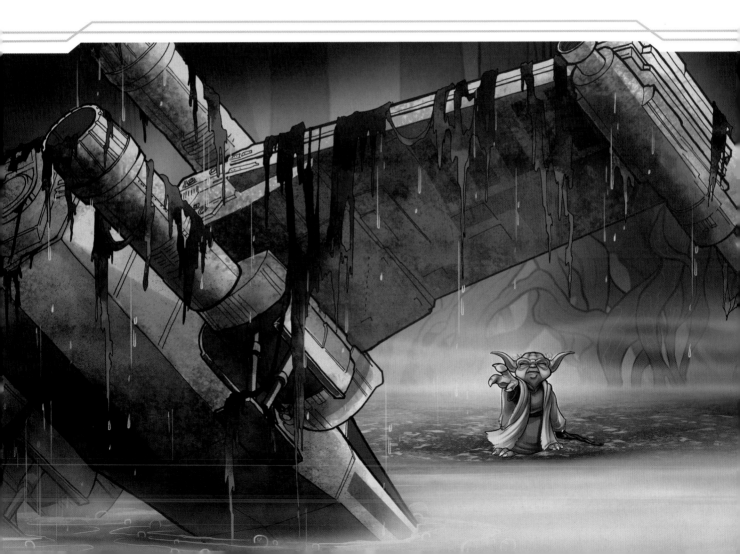

Luke continued his training, more determined than ever. One day, he saw a vision through the Force. His friends Han Solo and Princess Leia were in trouble! They had been captured by Darth Vader.

"It is the future you see," Yoda explained.

"I've got to go to them," Luke insisted. He couldn't bear to think that Han and Leia were in danger.

Luke knew that a Jedi Knight was a defender, not an attacker. A Jedi acted out of protection rather than anger and always put other people ahead of himself. Although Yoda did not want him to leave, Luke felt that he had to help his friends.

Yoda wished that he had more time to help Luke prepare. He worried that Darth Vader would lure Luke to the dark side. But Luke believed he had come far enough in his training to make his own decisions. He would finish his training when his friends were safe.

"I'll return," he told Yoda. "I promise."

Luke's battles would not be easy, but he was good at heart. No matter where he went, the Force would be with him, always.

RESCUE FROM JABBA'S PALACE

HAN **SOLO** was in trouble. He had been captured by Darth Vader and frozen in carbonite. Then the bounty hunter Boba Fett had taken the frozen smuggler to the one place Han had been desperately trying to avoid: the palace of Jabba the Hutt.

Han owed Jabba a lot of money, and now Jabba wanted his revenge.

Han's friend Luke Skywalker came up with a rescue plan. He sent the droids R2-D2 and C-3PO to Jabba with a holographic message.

"Greetings, Exalted One," Luke said in the message. "I seek an audience with Your Greatness to bargain for Solo's life. As a token of my goodwill, I present to you a gift: these two droids."

Jabba looked at R2-D2 and C-3PO and laughed. "There will be no bargain," he said. "I will not give up my favorite decoration."

Jabba was not about to give up the droids, either. C-3PO was assigned to work as a translator in the palace, and R2-D2 was sent to Jabba's sail barge.

Later that night, as Jabba celebrated his victory over Han, a bounty hunter interrupted the party. C-3PO couldn't believe what he was seeing. The bounty hunter had captured Chewbacca, Han Solo's Wookiee friend.

Jabba was thrilled. He and the bounty hunter agreed on a price for Chewbacca, and Chewie was sent to the dungeon.

But this was no ordinary bounty hunter. It was Princess Leia in disguise!

That night, while everyone slept, she crept through Jabba's palace and freed Han from the carbonite.

"I've got to get you out of here," Leia said.

As she helped Han to his feet, an evil laugh filled the room. It was Jabba. He had them trapped!

Jabba made Leia a slave in his throne room. His servants took hold of the weakened Han and threw him in the dungeon with Chewie. The Wookiee was very happy to see his friend again.

The next day, Luke Skywalker himself arrived at Jabba's palace. Using his Jedi powers, he tried to trick Jabba into freeing his friends.

"You will bring Captain Solo and the Wookiee to me," Luke said. "I warn you not to underestimate my powers."

But the Jedi mind trick did not work on Jabba.

"There will be no bargain, young Jedi," Jabba replied. "I shall enjoy watching you die."

The floor opened beneath Luke, and he fell into a dark, musty pit.

Luke had tumbled into the lair of a vicious rancor. All around him were the bones of the monster's previous victims.

Suddenly, a gate opened. The rancor stomped into the pit and toward Luke.

The rancor picked up Luke in one hand and opened its giant mouth. But Luke was ready! He shoved a bone between the rancor's teeth so it couldn't bite down. Startled, the beast dropped him. Then, rushing past the beast, Luke threw a skull at the gate's controls. The gate slammed down, crushing the rancor.

Jabba was not happy. He had expected his monster to defeat the Jedi!

At Jabba's order, Luke, Han, and Chewie were brought before him.

"Jabba the Hutt has decreed that you are to be terminated . . . immediately," C-3PO translated. "You will be taken to the Dune Sea and cast into the Pit of Carkoon, the nesting place of the all-powerful Sarlacc."

On board Jabba's sail barge, R2-D2 watched as Jabba's guards prepared the prisoners. He recognized one of the guards. It was Han's old friend Lando in disguise!

Luke stepped onto the plank over the Sarlacc pit. With a nod to R2-D2, he jumped! Suddenly, R2-D2 shot an object into the sky. Luke grabbed the plank and sprang back onto the deck of Jabba's ship. Reaching out his hand, he caught the object that R2-D2 had thrown.

It was his lightsaber!

Luke, Han, and Chewie wasted no time. The three jumped into battle with Jabba's men, hurling them overboard and into the mouth of the Sarlacc.

Inside Jabba's barge, Princess Leia seized her moment to escape. Wrapping her chain around the evil monster, she defeated him once and for all.

R2-D2 zapped Leia's chain and freed her.

While Luke fought off the rest of Jabba's men, Leia aimed the barge cannon at the deck. Then, holding on to each other, Luke and Leia swung to safety.

Reunited at last, the heroes escaped across the desert of Tatooine. Behind them, Jabba's barge exploded.

They had defeated Jabba. But more important, they had rescued Han. They were a team again.

THE EWOKS
JOIN THE FIGHT

THE REBELS were on a special mission on the forest moon of Endor. Princess Leia, Luke Skywalker, Han Solo, Chewbacca, R2-D2, and C-3PO were looking for a special bunker. Inside was a shield generator that could help them destroy the evil Empire's Death Star!

As the rebels snuck through the forest, they spotted two Imperial biker scouts. The scouts were patrolling the woods around the bunker.

"Chewie and I will take care of this," Han said, pointing to the scouts. "You stay here."

But as soon as Han and Chewie attacked, more scouts appeared. The scouts jumped on their speeder bikes and zoomed off to warn Darth Vader.

Luke and Leia jumped aboard two other bikes.

"Keep on that one. I'll take these two," Luke called as he sped away.

Leia chased after the other scout. She managed to catch up to him, but he fired his blaster at her and she was thrown from her speeder. She was all alone in the forest, with no way to get back to her friends.

Suddenly, a small furry creature appeared. He was an Ewok. He poked at Leia with a sharp stick.

"Cut it out," Leia said, standing up and brushing herself off.

The Ewok seemed to be afraid of her.

"I won't hurt you," Leia said. "Here. Want something to eat?"

The Ewok was just getting comfortable with Leia when a biker scout appeared behind her! The Ewok quickly hid behind a log.

"Freeze!" the scout said.

From his hiding place, the Ewok hit the trooper with a large stick. Leia used the distraction to disarm the scout.

"Come on. Let's get out of here," Leia said.

The Ewok took Leia's hand and led her toward his village.

Meanwhile, Luke and his friends searched for Leia. But all they found was a wrecked speeder and Leia's helmet.

While they were looking for Leia, a group of Ewoks found *them*! The Ewoks tied up the rebels and took them to their village.

When they arrived, the rebels were surprised to see Princess Leia! Leia tried to tell the Ewoks that Han, Luke, and Chewie were her friends, but they did not listen. They only seemed interested in C-3PO. They thought he was a powerful being.

"Threepio," Luke said, "tell them if they don't do as you wish, you'll become angry and use your magic."

C-3PO repeated Luke's message, but the Ewoks still refused to free his friends.

Closing his eyes, Luke used the Force to lift C-3PO into the air.

The Ewoks were amazed. This proved to them that the droid was very powerful. They quickly did as he said and untied Luke, Han, and Chewie.

That night, the Ewoks gathered around C-3PO, who told them tales of the rebels and Darth Vader.

The Ewoks liked the stories. And they liked the rebels.

One of the Ewoks jumped up and began to hug Han. As he did so, the little creature jabbered away.

"He says the Ewoks are going to show us the quickest way to the shield generator," C-3PO translated.

The next morning, when the rebels and the Ewoks set out for the shield generator, Luke did not go along. He knew it was time to face Darth Vader. Leia said good-bye to him and wished him luck.

Soon the rebels and the Ewoks arrived at the bunker where the generator was located. But the landing platform was surrounded by guards!

Luckily, the Ewoks knew of a back entrance. The rebels snuck around and surprised the Imperial scouts, quickly disarming them.

Han, Chewie, and Leia made their way deep inside the bunker. But before they could turn off the Death Star's shield generator, they were surrounded by Imperial soldiers. It was a trap! The Empire had been waiting for them.

The Ewoks watched as Imperial soldiers marched Han, Leia, and Chewie back out of the bunker. The Ewoks knew they had to help their friends.

Along with C-3PO, the Ewoks distracted the soldiers, drawing them away from Leia, Han, and Chewie. Then the Ewoks attacked.

They threw rocks at the stormtroopers.

They tripped them.

They tied them up.

With the Empire's soldiers taken care of, the rebels did what they had set out to do. Han Solo blew up the bunker and the shield generator inside. The Death Star was no longer protected.

Thanks to the Ewoks, the rebels could destroy the Death Star and defeat the Empire— once and for all!

Contents

Welcome to Kensington Palace

Kensington Palace from the south east by John Buckler, 1826.

...a place of secret stories and public lives. Built as a royal home for newly-weds William III and Mary II at the end of the 17th century, Kensington has been a stage for the drama of the nation's history, with private scenes of love, loss, heartbreak and happiness played out within these elegant walls. Now comes a new chapter in the story. Major changes are happening here. A huge new garden reconnects the landscape and the palace. Inside, intriguing new routes connect the fabulous state rooms and many surprises await.

Welcome to Kensington, a palace for everyone.

What to see

To help you make the most of your day at Kensington Palace, follow our guide to the four routes through palace history, along with some special moments you won't want to miss.

Tour 1:
The King's State Apartments

Take the journey of a courtier through the splendid King's State Apartments. Climb the magnificent King's Staircase where Georgian courtiers peer down from William Kent's spectacular design. Enjoy the impressively decorated rooms beyond and marvel at the exquisite 18th-century court dress. Pages 16-23

Tour 2:
The Queen's State Apartments

In the Queen's State Apartments we lift the curtain on the lives of Mary II, Queen Anne and the House of Stuart. This was a private family with personal secrets, reflected in the architecture of the intimate wooden panelled rooms in which they lived. Pages 26-9

Tour 3:
Victoria Revealed

Explore the story of the woman behind the Crown, in the rooms where Queen Victoria grew up. This permanent display explores Victoria's life from her lonely childhood at the palace to her final years. Hear in her own words Victoria's deep love for Albert and the dreadful impact of his sudden death. Pages 32-7

Tour 4:

Modern royals

In a series of changing displays we celebrate the style of some of Kensington's most famous modern residents, including Princess Diana and Princess Margaret. Pages 46-51

And don't miss...

The palace gardens

The palace gardens have been transformed to reconnect the building with its landscape, providing fantastic new vistas and picturesque walks to delight you. Pages 58-61

History where it happened

Look out for history 'hotspots' around the palace, where events took place that shaped the nation: from the intimate closet where a queen argued with her best friend, to the grand salon where a princess picked up the reins of government. Find out more in our leaflet or by talking to our Explainers, who you will meet during your visit.

A short history of
Kensington Palace

Kensington Palace has been many things during its three hundred year existence. Most importantly it has been a setting for the royal court, but also a seat of power and a venue for personal rivalry and intrigue.

It has been a museum and even a barracks for soldiers guarding the Great Exhibition. At all times, for kings and courtiers to humble servants, it has been a home. This is a quality it retains to the present day, in unbroken continuity.

When Kensington was a small village remote from the capital, and open fields stretched as far as the eye could see, a modest courtier's mansion known as Nottingham House stood here. In 1689, after the bloodless coup of the 'Glorious Revolution' had swept away King James II (1685-8), the new joint monarchs, King William III (1689-1702) and Queen Mary II (1689-94), known to posterity as William & Mary, immediately set about finding a new, private country home, where they could retreat from the old and rambling official palace of Whitehall. They purchased Nottingham House from Daniel Finch, William's trusted Secretary of State, for £20,000. Within weeks the architect Sir Christopher Wren was set to work transforming the house into a suitable royal residence. The new palace was furnished with a chapel, accommodation for courtiers, kitchens, stables, barracks, but above all, a

series of grand rooms or State Apartments where the King and Queen could hold audiences and ceremonies of state.

Queen Mary is overshadowed by her husband. Her brief reign has left little impression in Britain's national consciousness, but she was extensively involved in the design and furnishing of the palace. Echoes of her taste remain, most visible in the few pieces of her vast collection of oriental porcelain that survive. During the construction, she visited almost every day, keen to 'hasten the workmen', and impatient to finish. Work proceeded so rapidly that part of the building collapsed killing one workman and injuring several others. The whole project then nearly ended in disaster in November 1691 when fire broke out in the courtiers' lodgings, burning out a whole wing before being brought under control, extinguished with water carried in broken-open bottles from the beer cellar. By 1692 the building neared completion, with a new gallery and staircase for the Queen, as well as rooms for her maids of honour. Within two years, the greatest calamity occurred, when at the end of 1694, Queen Mary died of smallpox in her bedchamber at the palace.

William lost interest in the building after Mary's death, but he did complete the compact and very beautiful range that overlooks the south, housing his picture gallery with private apartments on the lower floors. It was furnished, the diarist John Evelyn noted, 'with all the best pictures'. In 1698,

Above left: Medal commemorating the coronation of William and Mary, 1689.

Below right: Bronze statue of William III, presented to Edward VII in 1907.

Opposite: This recently discovered painting of fallow deer in the royal paddock at Kensington, by an unknown artist, c1695, is the earliest-known view of William III's newly-completed palace.

This early 18th-century view shows Kensington Palace and its gardens as laid out for William and Mary at the end of the 17th century. The Orangery to the north, was added by Queen Anne in the early years of her reign.

A mid-18th century view of Kensington Palace by an unknown artist showing the lawns sweeping right up to the palace. Following the death of George II in 1760, the State Apartments lay silent and neglected for over a hundred years.

the King entertained the Russian Tsar Peter the Great here during his visit to England, though Peter was far more interested in the King's wind-dial, which survives above the fireplace, than in the art.

The short reign of William's successor Queen Anne (1702-14) saw few alterations to the palace, but many modifications to the gardens. Anne's greatest contribution was the Orangery, constructed in 1704-5, designed as a greenhouse for her orange trees but used as a venue for balls and ceremonies. In the private rooms that her sister Mary had built, Anne most famously ended her relationship with her closest friend Sarah Churchill, Duchess of Marlborough in 1710 (see page 30). On 1 August 1714, at the age of 49, Anne died at Kensington.

Despite the prodigious achievement of 17 pregnancies, Anne left no direct heir, and the throne passed to a distant relative, Georg Ludwig, Elector of Hanover, who descended though his grandmother from King James I (1603-25). The new King George I (1714-27), on visiting Kensington for the first time, pronounced that he 'lik'd it very much', but surveys found the old building in very poor condition and plans were put in hand to rebuild it on a much larger scale. Ultimately, a more modest proposal saw a new set of State Apartments replace the old Jacobean house in 1718-22. The pedimented façade above the entrance on the East Front is the most visible testimony to these changes today.

Further embellishment took place between 1724 and 1726 when the rising young artist, William Kent, was given a commission to paint the ceilings of the state rooms with mythological and 'grotesque' scenes. Despite fierce criticism, the King approved of Kent's work, and so launched the career of one of the most influential architects, artists and garden designers of the 18th century. Kent also probably oversaw the expansion of the palace to the north-west, with a series of apartments or 'houses' around two courtyards. One of these was occupied by the King's mistress, others by his family.

The native American chief, Tomo Chachi (pictured here with his nephew Toonahowi) created a stir when he visited the palace with his tribe in 1734, their faces 'most hideously painted [in] black and red'.

Kensington's greatest period of prominence came during the reign of King George II (1727-60) and his consort, Queen Caroline. Unlike his father, George II enjoyed court ceremonies and entertained in style, and the gorgeously arrayed rooms that Kent had so recently finished were pressed fully into use. In 1734, the King and Queen met a delegation led by the native American chieftain Tomo Chachi, with the proprietors and settlers of the new colony Georgia, named after the King.

After Queen Caroline's death in 1734, the court lost much of its sparkle and Horace Walpole noted that 'the king has locked up half the palace since the Queen's death'. On 25 October 1760, George II died in his private apartments at Kensington (see page 57), and the brief heyday of the palace came to an end.

George II enjoyed court ceremonies and entertained in style.

This portrait of George II by Robert Edge Pine was painted at Kensington in 1759, the year before the King's dramatic death at the palace.

Kensington Palace in the 19th century took on a new life as home to minor royals and courtiers. Princess Victoria was born here in 1819 and lived at the palace until she became queen in 1837.

Princess Victoria with her mother Victoria, Duchess of Kent by Henry Bone, c1824.

Princess Victoria was born in the palace in 1819 and spent her formative years here in beautifully furnished apartments on the first and upper floors.

George III (1760-1820) showed little interest in Kensington, though for most of his reign the gilt furnishings and many paintings remained untouched in the darkened rooms. From the 1790s, however, parts of the palace found a new role as a home for two of his sons: the eccentric but popular Prince Augustus, Duke of Sussex and Edward, Duke of Kent. Sussex was a noted book collector, amassing over 50,000 volumes in his apartment. His brother, the Duke of Kent, a much less attractive figure, most famously did his country one indispensable service by fathering the future Queen Victoria. The Princess was born in the palace in 1819 and spent her formative years here in beautifully furnished apartments on the first and upper floors. In June 1837, she was woken at Kensington Palace to be told of her accession, and held her first council in the Red Saloon.

In the later 19th century, Kensington continued its role as a royal dormitory, housing Queen Victoria's daughters Princess Louise and Princess Beatrice (see page 46). Louise was a gifted artist and left an important legacy in the form of the statue of the young Queen Victoria (right), which graces the east side of the palace. Both princesses lived well into the 20th century and were joined by several of the Queen's grandchildren, including Princess Alice of Athlone, who died in 1981 (see page 48), the last of Victoria's grandchildren to die.

Over time, the State Apartments gradually became denuded of furniture and pictures, but a major restoration took place in 1898 under the orders of Queen Victoria, and in 1912 they were filled with display cases when the palace became home to the London Museum. During the Second World War, incendiary bombs set light to the building and it was only due to the bravery of the palace's fire-watcher that the flames were contained. In the 1960s, Princess Margaret came to live at Kensington, holding her own miniature court of artists, entertainers and playwrights, while other members of the Royal Family arrived through the 1970s and 1980s. The most famous of these were the Prince and Princess of Wales. Princess Diana lived at Kensington until her death in 1997, and her sons the princes William and Harry spent some of their formative years in the private apartments on the north side of the palace. In 2011, a newly-married Prince William returned to his childhood home, bringing his wife Catherine, Duchess of Cambridge to live here.

Kensington has always been a place with two faces: one public, the other private. For many years, the Museum of London occupied much of the public space, but after its departure in 1976 these great rooms were gradually brought back to their original condition. This is a process that continues to the present day. Today, more of the building than ever has been opened to the public and Kensington is again more visible and welcoming as it was in the past. Despite its grandeur, it also remains a place that people may call home.

Above: Princess Margaret in her garden at Kensington Palace, 1965.

Left: This iconic statue of Queen Victoria in her coronation robes, which sits on the east side of the palace, was designed by her daughter Princess Louise and unveiled by the Queen in 1893.

A survival guide

You may look the part, but do you think you can pass into the presence of the monarch with just a small bribe and a big smile? Think again. Serious social climbers read on...

The Great Drawing Room lies at the heart of the Georgian royal palace. Here the king mingles most evenings with his guests, and the winners (and losers) of the Georgian age can calculate precisely how high they have climbed (or fallen) by the warmth of their reception at court.

Although the power of Parliament is rapidly growing, ambitious and talented people still flock to court in search of perks and prestige. They understand all the nuances of court etiquette and know how to manipulate them to their advantage.

It's vital, therefore, to learn the rules of the game.

Right: A young woman and her husband attending an 18th-century court gala.

1 What should you wear?

Ladies have to wear the court uniform: the 'mantua', a coat-like dress with a train behind, spread out sideways over an immensely wide petticoat supported by a hoop. Tightly-laced, uncomfortable and incredibly heavy, its skirts get wider and wider as the 18th century progresses. Your arms descend from a requisite three rows of frills. ('I am so incommoded with these nasty ruffles!' says Fanny Burney, English novelist of the era.) You should wear your best jewels, feathers in your hair and carry a fan.

Gentlemen should wear a wig, an embroidered suit, silk stockings, and court pumps decorated with glittery buckles. However, you can gate-crash a court party quite easily if you borrow the right clothes and slip a shilling to the footman on the door. You can even hire a sword from a booth at the entrance. 'Dress is a very foolish thing', declares the arch-courtier Lord Chesterfield, and yet, at the same time, 'it is a very foolish thing for a man not to be well dressed'.

Tip: you can't be overdressed.

Above: A pair of late 18th-century ladies' shoes of purple and ivory kid. The elegant cut decoration of the leather helps to emphasise the fashionable pointed toe.

Court

2 How do you walk in a dress like that?

It's quite hard to walk in a mantua, and only grand palace doorways have the width to accommodate the hooped skirts without the need to turn sideways. The whalebone hoops force you to take tiny steps, so court ladies are described as looking like they roll along on wheels. Ladies-in-waiting aren't allowed to sit down, or to fold their arms. Before exiting the royal presence they have to curtsey three times, and then back out of the room. But don't worry: your dancing master will train you in how to do all this.

Tip: take tiny, elegant steps, and practise beforehand.

Right: The 'Rockingham mantua', a spectacular silver court dress worn in about 1765 and costing more than £10,000 in today's money.

'I am so incommoded with these nasty ruffles!'

Below: A porcelain bourdaloue, c1735-40, essential for a long day at court.

How on earth does one relieve oneself?

It's easier than it looks, as you won't be wearing knickers (not invented yet). You may squat over a chamberpot, or else you use a 'bourdaloue'. This is a little jug like a gravy boat that you clench between your thighs. Privacy is not essential, and the French ambassador's wife annoys everyone with the 'frequency and quantity of her pissing which she does not fail to do at least ten times a day amongst a cloud of witnesses'.

However, if the queen doesn't grant you permission to go, you just have to try to hold on. One of Queen Caroline's ladies was once defeated by a bursting bladder that 'threatened the shoes of bystanders'.

Tip: take a 'bourdaloue' with you.

What messages can I signal with my fan?

Most people think that the secret language of the fan – 'beware, my husband approaches', 'you are cruel', 'don't forget me' – is a Victorian invention. But there are hints that it was already in place in the 1720s. According to the language of the fan, the ladies painted by William Kent on the walls at Kensington Palace (see front cover) are all saying variations of the same thing: 'I am married', 'I wish to get rid of you' or just plain 'no'.

Either this is a very strange coincidence, or else Kent is playing a joke in depicting all these ravishing ladies making such cruel denials!

Tip: don't wave your fan about without forethought!

Who should I cultivate?

The court is not really a meritocracy, and to acquire a post in the royal household you will need a powerful patron. You must wait for the right opportunity to press your case for a job, a promotion or a favour. 'By the Grace of God', an ambitious court equerry promises himself, 'I am willing & ready to bustle thro' this bad world'. If a man 'can hold out five years', counsels another courtier, 'tis morally impossible he should not come into play'. But there is still a risk that you might end up penniless and jobless, having wasted 'half of the very flower' of your life standing waiting outside a door.

Tip: identify a patron as soon as you can.

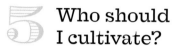

The Great Drawing Room, 'where all strangers, above the inferior rank, may see the King'.

6 How do I get home?

Leaving the Drawing Room at last, you need to search among the jostling sea of servants in the courtyard for your own chairmen and sedan chair. Ladies travelling by chair flip up their whalebone hoops on each side so that they look like strange winged insects. They also tilt their heads back and remain motionless so the roof doesn't squash their tall hair-dos. Exhausted by the hours of standing in their weighty dresses, they will go straight home to bed. Gentlemen, however, might not go home at all, but continue their networking in the clubs and coffee houses of St James's.

Tip: prepare for an exhausting evening!

Left: An 18th-century court fan was not just used for keeping cool. It became an essential part of a lady's body language and was used to send messages across a room, without saying a word.

15

Tour 1
The King's State Apartments

This sumptuous set of rooms, each grander than the last, leads to the heart of the court where the fortunate, and determined, might come face to face with the king.

The King's Staircase

The King's Staircase is the first link to the circuit of rooms making up the King's State Apartments. All the great and good of Georgian London would have climbed up these stairs to visit the king.

Visitors to court could only enter if their clothes and jewels passed muster with the guards. Some of the guards in their red uniforms stand among the figures of the arcade painted on the walls, many of them identifiable as members of the royal court (see front cover).

The staircase paintings were completed in 1724 by William Kent, in place of the plainer wooden panelling installed by Wren. This bumptious young man included a portrait of himself on the ceiling, in a brown turban and holding an artist's palette.

The imaginary architecture of the staircase painting was inspired by work that Kent had seen in the palaces of Rome, where he trained. The painted figure of Diana on the top landing is a copy of a real antique statue – the original, owned by Kent's friend Thomas Coke, is at Holkham Hall in Norfolk.

The Presence Chamber

This room contains the nearest thing to a throne that you'll see at Kensington today – a gilded armchair that belonged to George II's son, Frederick. Here, important guests would be ushered into the royal presence to bow and kiss the king's hand.

The most famous visitors received in this room were Chief Tomo Chachi and his war-captains from the Cherokee nation. The British had recently founded the southern American colony

Detail of the Grinling Gibbons' overmantel carvings in the Presence Chamber.

of Georgia, named after the King himself, on land where the Cherokees lived. The Cherokees came to present the King with 'sticks with feathers on them, which are emblems of peace', their faces 'most hideously painted [in] black and red'.

Here, William Kent's grotesque-style ceiling was inspired by the decorations found in Roman houses that had recently been excavated on the Palatine Hill in Rome. (People thought that these houses were caves, or grottoes, so this style's name is based on a misunderstanding.) But the room's decorative highlight is the limewood carvings by Grinling Gibbons surrounding the fireplace. These cherubs with closed eyes and beautiful roses were originally (oddly, to our eyes) painted white.

Right: Apollo in his chariot from the ceiling of the Presence Chamber.

Left: The King's Staircase, decorated by William Kent and completed in 1724. The 18th-century writer Horace Walpole was very critical of Kent's work and grudgingly described the staircase as 'the least defective work of his pencil'.

Left: The Privy Chamber was one of three new rooms added to the State Apartments in 1718-22 for George I.

Opposite: View from the Privy Chamber to the Cupola Room and the magnificent clock known as *The Temple of the Four Grand Monarchies of the World.*

Much more lies beyond this first room, and visitors to court would pray that the guards on each successive door would let them pass. In here, however, we meet the State Apartments' most important residents: George II and his wife Queen Caroline, in the form of life-filled terracotta busts by Michael Rysbrack, made in 1738 and 1739. The spirit of Caroline, in particular, fills the next rooms you are about to see.

The remaining spaces in the State Apartments form a circuit of parade. Often bare of furniture, these rooms would have been filled to overflowing with people on the days that the court was in attendance.

The Privy Chamber

This room was one of Queen Caroline's favourite entertaining spaces. Its magnificent ceiling, painted by William Kent in 1723, shows Mars, the Roman god of War, and Minerva the goddess of wisdom, surrounded by emblems representing the arts and sciences. For Mars, read King George who was the last king to lead his troops into battle; for Minerva, read Queen Caroline who invited many artists and scientists to court. Arranged around the room are the marble busts of her contemporary heroes that she commissioned from Giovanni Battista Guelphi: scientists Sir Isaac Newton, John Locke and Robert Boyle, and clerics William Wollaston

and Samuel Clarke. Originally, they decorated the Hermitage, a rustic garden pavilion created for Queen Caroline in what are now Kew Gardens.

The impressive tapestries in this room come from a set representing the seasons made at the Mortlake Tapestry workshop founded by King Charles I (1625-49). The tapestries here show the months of February, July and August, and November.

A mysterious moor

The striking bust of a moor, made from coloured stones by John Nost the Elder, is a survival from the collection of William III. Perhaps a portrait of a member of William's household, the bust's carved stone collar shows he was a slave. We are hoping to find out more about who he was and how he came to be celebrated in such a gorgeous way.

The strange object in the centre of the room is a clock, a music box that plays Handel and an artwork to boot. The pictures on the sides depict four monarchies from antiquity.

The Cupola Room

The most splendidly-decorated room in the palace, this marks a great new beginning in the history of design.

The Cupola Room was the first royal commission of William Kent, the artist and designer who would go on first to decorate the rest of the State Apartments, and then to create a distinctive visual look for the Georgian age. Here, he re-created in paint a baroque Roman palace but with the Star of the Order of the Garter as the ceiling's centrepiece.

Kent had just returned from ten years in Rome, so he knew that in Italy painters were creating architectural effects. In fact, this room marks the moment that the art of interior decoration, as opposed to painting, was born.

Kent was a surprising choice. Everyone thought that George I would choose the established painter, Sir James Thornhill. But Thornhill was expensive and Kent undercut him on price. Thornhill's friends tried to get Kent sacked by complaining about the quality of his work. The gilded statues, they said, made a 'terrible glaring show'. The King, however, was pleased with Kent's work and asked him to complete the other rooms.

The strange object in the centre of the room is a clock, a music box that plays Handel and an artwork to boot. The pictures on the sides depict four monarchies from antiquity. Completed in 1743, it was bought by Princess Augusta, George II's daughter-in-law. Rysbrack had a hand in this work, but more impressive is his carved overmantel above the fireplace showing a Roman wedding, that dates from 1723-4.

The most celebrated gathering in this room occurred in 1819 for the baptism of Princess Victoria. Her uncle the Prince Regent (later King George IV) joined the infant's parents, the Duke and Duchess of Kent, and it was the surly Prince Regent himself who – having rejected a series of suitably royal names – decided she should be called Alexandrina (after the Russian Tsar) Victoria (after her mother).

Top: The ceiling of the King's Drawing Room by William Kent, 1722.

Above: *William Kent* (detail) by Bartholomew Dandridge, c1730.

Giorgio Vasari's *Venus and Cupid*, *c*1543, the so-called 'Fat Venus' that caused a huge row between George II and Queen Caroline in 1735.

The King's Drawing Room

Try to imagine this empty room packed absolutely full with courtiers, all come to the king's parties in search of power and patronage. It's the climax of the whole suite of rooms, and the avenues in Kensington Gardens converge upon its central window.

On the ceiling William Kent has shown the powerful god Jupiter, who accidentally killed his lover Semele. The message is clear – watch out! This is the epicentre of power. Portraits of Venetian doges – rulers who could not compete with Britain's – line the walls.

Next door was the king's bedchamber, and halfway through the evening he would come out to make his appearance. Guests would form themselves into a circle, hoping to speak to him. If you were lucky, one of the high court officers would introduce you to the king.

This room was the location for a famous royal argument. In 1735, King George was away in Hanover. Queen Caroline, the art lover, seized the opportunity to reorganise the pictures and hung Sir Anthony van Dyck's beautiful portraits of the Stuart royal family here. When George returned, he was furious and insisted that the Italian paintings be replaced. Lord Hervey, a courtier who had been party to Caroline's plan, asked whether this even meant the painting of Venus and Cupid by Vasari (a copy of a painting by Michelangelo). The King replied angrily that yes, he meant his 'Fat Venus'. She is still there.

The Council Chamber

Located in one of Christopher Wren's pavilions, built on to the corners of the original Nottingham House, this room served William III, George I and George II, as a meeting place for the Privy Council. By 1811 it had fallen into such disrepair that major renovation was needed to make it less 'dangerous' and the columns were added as supports. The sort of court dress that would once have been worn in these state rooms is on display here.

Queen Caroline's Closet

This small room has a history that is bigger than its size. Originally, it was William III's Little Bedchamber; cosier than the State Bedchamber next door. George I used the room to store books, but these were banished after Queen Caroline made one of the most important art history discoveries of the era. In 1727, she found hidden in a cabinet a portfolio containing many drawings made by Hans Holbein the Younger of Henry VIII and his courtiers. Caroline made this room a Gallery of the English. With the Holbein drawings as star exhibits she crowded the walls with three hundred small paintings, miniatures and embroideries.

By the end of the 18th century all these treasures had been moved to decorate other royal homes and the room was subsequently converted to make dressing rooms for the Duchess of Kent and a bathroom for Princess Victoria.

The King's Gallery

The King's Gallery was built for William III as an addition to Wren's original design in the new South Front and was finished in about 1700. Originally, it was hung with green velvet, and William would meet his spies and plan his military campaigns here. In 1694 Robert Morden had made the charming wind-dial, attached with chains and pulleys to a weather vane on the roof. The King could see whether the wind was set fair for an invasion fleet to come up the English Channel. The room saw many intimate moments. It was here that William played soldiers with his little nephew and intended heir, the Duke of Gloucester and, after a riding accident at Hampton Court, it was here that the King caught the chill that led to his death on 8 March 1702.

The gallery was transformed in 1725 by William Kent for George I. Red damask replaced the green velvet, the fine oak joinery was painted white and gilded, a new marble chimneypiece, carved overmantel and new door cases were inserted. Kent and his assistants painted the seven large ceiling canvases that show scenes from the life of Ulysses.

The picture frames and the stands for the statues were also designed by Kent. Most of the pictures, then as now, were Italian and dated from the 16th and early 17th century. They include Tintoretto's *Esther before Ahasuerus* and *The Muses*. At the eastern end hung the original (now a copy) of van Dyck's monumental *Charles I with M. St Antoine*. George I inspected the gallery shortly after it was completed. He was said to be 'well pleased' with Kent's work.

In 1835 the gallery was controversially divided at the instruction of the Duchess of Kent to make three new rooms for Princess Victoria. Although her uncle, King William IV (1830-7), was furious at the audacity of this, Victoria herself was delighted. She recorded in her diary her pleasure at 'three lofty, fine cheerful rooms. One... is my sitting-room and is very prettily furnished indeed'. The partitions were removed later in the 19th century to reveal Kent's grand scheme once more.

Left: *William III when Prince of Orange* (detail) by William Wissing, 1685.

Right: William III celebrated his 50th birthday at Kensington, where there were 'Entertainments for the Ladies, and other Persons of Quality in the Great Gallery'.

It was here that William played soldiers with his little nephew and it was here that the King caught the chill that led to his death on 8 March 1702.

'Very noble, tho'not greate'

John Evelyn

Kensington's quiet stylistic revolution

A charming suburban villa provided the basis for Kensington Palace, which may be why despite all the stylish additions and flamboyant interior décor, it remains at heart a royal home.

In 1689 Kensington House remained a Jacobean villa on the edge of town – an unlikely beginning for a royal palace, let alone a showcase for some of England's most brilliant architects. Over the years some even drew up grandiose proposals to demolish this suburban home to make way for an English Versailles, but these all came to nothing. Kensington remained essentially a royal home because of the nature of British monarchy. Architects from the Office of Works (the state building department) – often the very best – were expected to do as the king required, but during this period, the royal purse rarely bulged and British monarchs could also ill-afford the political cost of lavish building projects.

First came Christopher Wren with one of his typically ingenious compromises to satisfy William and Mary, who needed a new palace in a hurry. He added four large brick pavilions at the corners of the existing house so that the old house was almost buried. This must have pleased the royal couple, newly arrived from their Dutch homes that included the hunting lodge at Het Loo, which too featured similar brick pavilions. Wren's Kensington was downright plain in its detail, only relieved on the inside by the rich décor created under Mary's personal supervision – and now largely gone.

Six years later – after Mary's death – the King renewed his interest in the palace, but this time it was Wren's former 'Gentleman', his talented assistant Nicholas Hawksmoor, who at last added grandeur along the whole South Front. He presented the King with his cardboard model of the King's Gallery, with its giant brick pilasters and urns above, in the baroque style that was breaking out all over England.

With the arrival of Queen Anne came that other stellar baroque architect, John Vanbrugh. In 1702 he was made her Comptroller, with only one major building to his credit, having an unpromising career path to date of soldier, prisoner, spy, playwright and later, theatre-owner. Vanbrugh seems to have been given the task of devising a magnificent orangery for Anne, but the more experienced Hawksmoor worked up his scheme and probably devised its elegantly-proportioned interiors, which were actually used for banquets and even 'touching for the evil', a superstition that the Queen revived.

After Anne's death at Kensington the new king, George I, found it very comfortable for entertaining his court, but was thwarted when the new surveyor, a Whig party placeman, William Benson, declared the old house 'much cracked and out of repair'. He rebuilt the main state rooms in a sober Palladian style, almost certainly assisted by its chief

proponent, Colen Campbell. Their design added dignity to the palace, in contrasting grey-brown brick, but with little flair. This was left to another upstart, the painter William Kent, who had flagrantly ousted the best man for the job, Sir James Thornhill. Fresh from Italy, Kent transformed the King's rooms with a series of sometimes disconcerting paintings. Although he could only paint his architecture at this point, Kent did introduce a revolution in British houses, by designing complete interiors from the walls to the furniture, even ball gowns. And Kensington was the greatest advertisement a new talent like his could get.

Top: *The Orangery* by Henry Parke, c1815.

Centre left: *Sir Christopher Wren* (detail) by Sir Godfrey Kneller, 1711.

Centre right: *Sir John Vanbrugh* (detail) by Thomas Murray, c1718.

Bottom: The ceiling of the Cupola Room.

25

Tour 2
The Queen's State Apartments

These cosy, private rooms were used by Queen Mary II for relaxation. Here, she enjoyed spending time with her husband and ladies-in-waiting away from the hustle and bustle of the court. Later inhabitants continued this intimate theme.

The Queen's Staircase

The Queen's Apartments are deliberately plainer and lower-key than the King's, both inside and out. The oak-panelled Queen's Staircase is a sharp contrast to the grand marble King's Staircase. Its note of quiet domesticity perfectly matches the taste of Queen Mary for whom these apartments were built by Christopher Wren between 1689 and 1694.

Mary would have glided down the elegant shallow treads of this staircase – the first known example of an open string stair where the banisters rise directly from the treads – to reach her beloved gardens through the door at its foot.

The Queen's Gallery

Beautiful and fashionable Mary arrived in London and was crowned queen at just 28. Her marriage in 1677 to her cousin William, Stadtholder of the Netherlands, had started badly: she cried for days after hearing that this match had been made. William was twice her age, was a chronic asthmatic, lived in another country and spoke another language. But they became a loving couple. Portraits of Mary and William by William Wissing hang in the gallery, together with a portrait of Mary's mother, Anne Hyde, Duchess of York, by Sir Peter Lely.

It was in the Netherlands that Mary developed her passion for collecting treasures from India, China and Japan, the fruits of trade by the Dutch East India Company. When it came to furnishing her new apartments at Kensington Palace these were given pride of place. She filled the gallery

Left: The tulip was very popular during the reign of William and Mary and the Queen's collection of ceramics included several pagoda-shaped vases in which these flowers were displayed.

Above: The installation in the Queen's Gallery today is inspired by the song birds that Mary kept in the gallery in velvet-trimmed cages.

Opposite: *Mary II when Princess of Orange* (detail) by William Wissing, 1685.

Queen Mary amassed a collection of thousands of pieces of porcelain and Delft. Some 787 pieces were put on display at Kensington Palace; the effect must have been quite magnificent.

with sumptuous artefacts: Turkish carpets, embroidered hangings and lacquer furniture. Her collection of oriental porcelain was crowded on to every surface; there were over 150 pieces in this room alone.

Queen Mary used the gallery for recreation and it was often filled with her ladies-in-waiting working at their embroidery, while one of them read aloud. There were bird cages upholstered in red velvet set up in the windows and velvet cushions scattered across the floor for her cherished dogs.

Among the guests who visited the gallery was Peter the Great, Tsar of Russia who had been invited to court by William III in 1698. William persuaded his guest to sit for a portrait by

Sir Godfrey Kneller, which still hangs in this room. Looking at this majestic portrait, few would guess how badly behaved the Tsar was during his stay. While in England, Peter lodged with the diarist John Evelyn, who later complained that nearly every window in his house had been smashed, his paintings had bullet holes in them, and all of his chairs – and most of his staircase – had been chopped up for firewood.

The Queen's Closet

The closet was a room to withdraw into from the social world of the gallery. It was here that a terrible argument took place between Queen Anne and her childhood friend and confidante, Sarah Churchill, Duchess of Marlborough (see page 30).

While in England, Peter lodged with the diarist John Evelyn, who later complained that nearly every window in his house had been smashed.

Peter the Great, Tsar of Russia (detail) by Sir Godfrey Kneller, 1698.

Queen Anne by Sir Godfrey Kneller, *c*1702.
This portrait was used as the – not very flattering –
model for coinage and medals.

Anne was Mary II's younger sister and became
queen after William III died in 1702. As sovereign,
Anne used the King's Apartments and the Queen's
Apartments were adapted for her consort, Prince
George of Denmark. As a result, the Queen's
Gallery range was known as the 'Denmark Wing'
well into the 20th century.

The Queen's Eating Room

The beautiful panelling in this room survives
from the 17th century and shows how cosy and
domestic the queen's rooms once were. Here,
William and Mary would share simple private
suppers of fish and beer. Mary also doubtless
used this room to take tea, the newly-fashionable
hot drink, with the ladies of her household.

In keeping with the less grand atmosphere here,
the portrait over the mantelpiece is of a much-
loved housekeeper, Katherine Elliott painted by
John Riley in 1687-8. Katherine had been nurse
to the infant James II (Mary's father), and later
served as a court Dresser and Woman of the
Bedchamber to both his wives.

The Queen's Drawing Room

A list made in 1694 by Simon de Brienne, the
palace housekeeper, shows that Mary II had filled
this room with porcelain. Mary's enthusiasm for
ceramics led Daniel Defoe to make his famous
comment, 'The Queen brought about the

custom... of filling houses with China-ware
which increased to a strange degree afterwards
piling their China upon the tops of Cabinets,
Scutores, and every Chymney-Piece to the tops
of the Ceilings'.

Of all the rooms in this wing, the Drawing Room
has lost most of its original character. On the night
of 14 October 1940 it was badly damaged by an
incendiary bomb. The panelling was destroyed,
which is why the walls are now wallpapered.

The Queen's Bedroom

When William and Mary first moved into the
palace, this room was used by the Queen as
her State Bedroom. However, in 1691 almost as
soon as Christopher Wren had finished work
on the Queen's Apartments, Mary requested
that her rooms be extended, to provide her
with more accommodation. The additional work
included the Queen's Gallery and a new, private
bedchamber in a room beyond here.

No longer required as a bedchamber, this room
became another cosy sociable space where the
Queen could show off her treasures and the
chimneypiece was decorated with a display
of over 80 pieces of porcelain.

It was in the Queen's new bedchamber that Mary
tragically died in 1694 (see page 56). William,
who had refused to move from her side, slept
on a camp bed beside her, until the end.

When tea first arrived in England, its luxury status
and exotic, delicate flavour made it an instant hit with
women at court. Tea parties, like the one depicted here,
soon became a popular pastime.

'You may put it in writing'

Queen Anne and Sarah Churchill, Duchess of Marlborough

After a devastating row that shocked the Kensington court, Queen Anne refused to speak ever again to her dear friend Sarah Churchill. Was it politics or something more personal that split up the previously devoted pair?

On Good Friday 1710, Queen Anne and her one-time greatest friend met in the Queen's Closet at Kensington Palace. Sarah Churchill, Duchess of Marlborough pleaded for their old, intimate friendship to be maintained.

To every entreaty the Queen replied, 'You may put it in writing.' Sarah was so vexed at her royal mistress's unmoving silence that she said she was confident Anne 'would suffer in this world and the next for so much inhumanity', to which Anne answered 'that would be to herself'. They never saw each other again.

The pair met thirty-five years before their final falling-out, when Princess Anne was 10 and Sarah Jennings was 16, a Maid of Honour at Court. Three years later, Sarah married the dashing John Churchill, who would achieve fame as the victor in the wars against Louis XIV of France. Many stages of the relationship between these strong-willed women played out at Kensington. Escaping from royal protocol, to each other they were Mrs Morley and Mrs Freeman. When Anne came to the throne in 1702, it was said that Sarah moved from being 'merely the Princess of Denmark's familiar to... the evil genius of the whole state'. Anne showered Sarah with well-paid offices: Groom of the Stole, Mistress of the Robes, Keeper of the Privy Purse and Ranger of Windsor Great Park all in one. In her portraits, she proudly wears the gold key giving her privileged entry to the most private royal apartments. At Kensington, she was given a large apartment herself, which extended over two floors.

Keeping tight reins on expenditure, Sarah also kept hold of Anne's heart. The Queen wrote to 'my dear Mrs Freeman that I love more than words or actions can express... your poor unfortunate faithful Morley has a constant heart, loves you tenderly, passionately and sincerely'. We will never know whether this was physical or platonic, as most of Anne's letters were destroyed after she died; but we do know that love is fickle. Sarah Churchill also played an acute political role. This was the age when political parties were emerging. She advanced the Whig cause, influencing a naturally Tory-sympathising Anne and helping secure powerful offices for her associates. Eventually, the relationship came to its sad end. Sarah had meddled too much, and Queen Anne had a new favourite at Court, Abigail Masham, who had secretly married Prince George's servant at Kensington in 1707. Abigail was a Tory sympathiser, who worked her way into the Queen's affections and, according to Sarah Churchill's later slanders, her bed.

Opposite: A letter from Queen Anne to Sarah Churchill, 21 February 1703.

Sarah retired a bitter woman to build Blenheim Palace, her monument as well as memorial to her husband's victories. A key to this story is that all the protagonists were female. They fought for each other's affections; they had influence; but however much she wanted it, ultimately no woman could exercise the political power and leverage that a man could. Both women suffered in this world for the relationship they had and the position in society they occupied.

> She was confident Anne 'would suffer in this world and the next for so much inhumanity', to which Anne answered 'that would be to herself'. They never saw each other again.

Above: A playing card of c1711 showing Queen Anne bestowing the Office of Groom of the Stole – previously held by Sarah Churchill – on Sarah's rival Elizabeth Seymour, Duchess of Somerset.

Below: *Sarah Churchill, Duchess of Marlborough*, after Sir Godfrey Kneller, c1700. The Duchess wears at her waist, the golden key of the Keeper of the Privy Purse.

Tour 3
Victoria Revealed

To the little princess who first toddled, and then walked with increasing maturity and confidence through these elegant rooms, Kensington was a well-loved home. This permanent display tells Queen Victoria's story from her first days at the palace to her final years, and highlights key moments and themes in her life.

The Stone Staircase

On 24 May 1819 Princess Victoria was born at Kensington Palace, where she lived with her widowed mother, the Duchess of Kent. It was on this staircase that she met her cousin Prince Albert for the first time in 1836. She became queen at Kensington Palace shortly after her 18th birthday.

The Red Saloon

Victoria held her first Privy Council in the Red Saloon on the morning she became queen in 1837. Wearing a plain black silk dress in recognition of her uncle William IV's demise the previous night, the 18-year-old Queen was surrounded by a dense crowd of older, much more experienced men. The Duke of Wellington and her uncles, the dukes of Sussex and Cumberland, were there. Lord Melbourne, the Prime Minister had written a short speech for her to read, in which she promised to fulfil her duty. She offered a hand for her councillors to kiss, and signed her first official document with a shaky, somewhat tentative 'Victoria R'. Despite the intimidating circumstances, the diarist Charles Greville noted how the young Victoria handled the whole ceremony with 'perfect calmness and self-possession'. Having lived under the watchful eye of her controlling mother, this was Victoria's first day of real independence.

Falling in love

'My heart is quite going', wrote Victoria when her cousin Albert, Prince of Saxe-Coburg and Gotha arrived at Windsor in 1839. He was 'excessively handsome' with 'beautiful blue eyes, an exquisite nose and such a pretty mouth with delicate moustachios'. She proposed to him four days later, and he accepted. A whirlwind romance followed as they sang, danced and rode together. After Prince Albert returned to Germany a few weeks later they exchanged many letters and gifts, including miniature portraits. He sent a bust of himself by Emil Wolff that he had commissioned during his Grand Tour in Italy and a gold and porcelain orange blossom brooch. He also sent some of his compositions, which she played as she waited for him to return. They married in the Chapel Royal at St James's Palace on 10 February 1840. For the wedding, Victoria wore a simple court dress of ivory Spitalfields silk, trimmed with Honiton lace from Devon. She recorded the day in her journal: 'Oh! this was the happiest day of my life!'

The First Council of Queen Victoria (detail) by Sir David Wilkie, 1838. This event took place in the Red Saloon on the day of Victoria's accession to the throne. The Queen wore a black mourning dress but was depicted by the artist in white so that she stood out against the black coats of the councillors.

Above: *Prince Albert* by Sir William Ross, 1839.

Opposite: *Queen Victoria* (detail) by Thomas Sully, 1837-9.

The Royal Family at Osborne House, May 1857. The Queen died at Osborne in January 1901.

Queen Victoria's military tunic, c1856, described by *The Times* as 'a piquant and graceful costume'.

Family life

The death of Princess Victoria's father before her first birthday in 1820 left her to grow up at Kensington Palace alone with her mother, the Duchess of Kent. The Duchess and her manipulative equerry, Sir John Conroy, devised the 'Kensington System', an education regime that was designed both to prepare Victoria for her future role as Queen and – as some people saw it – to keep the Princess firmly under their control. Victoria was lonely at Kensington. She had virtually no friends her own age and was kept away from life at court. The beautifully-dressed dolls she made with her German governess Baroness Lehzen and her frequent trips to the theatre provided a much needed escape from this secluded childhood, which she later called her 'life of difficulties'. Victoria

and Albert were determined to raise their nine children differently. They were deeply involved in their education and encouraged them to play with other children. Victoria did not particularly like babies but she kept many mementoes of her children's early years, including scores of their baby shoes (see page 53) and tiny locks of their hair preserved in specially-made jewellery.

Duty and work

The young Queen showed an unwavering sense of duty when she allowed only three days' honeymoon after her wedding to Prince Albert, who she gently reminded that 'business can stop and wait for nothing'. She handled the constant stream of paperwork and correspondence with increasing support from her husband, who began to meet her ministers alongside her from 1841. Even during her many pregnancies, the Queen kept up to date with news and her daily despatches, which were locked in red, leather-bound boxes. She communicated frankly with her ministers, making her personal prejudices against them and other politicians known. Like the monarchs before her, Victoria was deeply aware of her public image. The grand portraits she commissioned and the clothing she wore for important public occasions helped to shape how people viewed her. In 1856, for example, she showed empathy for Crimean War troops by wearing a red, military-inspired riding jacket during a review.

Left: Prince Alfred and Princess Alice sketched by their mother, Queen Victoria.

The staircase

Victoria was woken by her mother at six in the morning in a room at the top of this staircase on 20 June 1837. She went into her sitting room – in her dressing gown – to where the Archbishop of Canterbury and Lord Conyngham, the Lord Chamberlain were waiting for her.

Queen Victoria receiving the news of her accession at Kensington Palace, 20 June 1837, by Henry Tadworth Wells, 1880.

'Lord Conyngham then acquainted me that my poor Uncle, the King, was no more, and had expired at 12 minutes p. 2 this morning, and consequently that I am Queen.'

Prince Albert and the Great Exhibition

Prince Albert set to work immediately after he married Queen Victoria in 1840. He attempted to streamline inefficiencies in the Royal Household, got involved in government affairs and frequently deputised for the Queen while she was pregnant. The Great Exhibition in 1851 would be his greatest work. The festival was held between May and October that year in Joseph Paxton's impressive Crystal Palace in Hyde Park. This showcase of technological and cultural achievements from around the world attracted over six million visitors. Victoria and Albert lent several items to the exhibition, including a superbly carved boxwood cradle, which they had commissioned for their sixth child, Princess Louise, in 1848. They also made lots of purchases, including a 116-piece dessert service by Minton & Co. Victoria was immensely proud of Albert's involvement in the exhibition. On the day of the opening, she wrote 'this is one of the greatest and most glorious days of our lives'.

> 'My life as a happy one is ended', wrote the grief-stricken Queen as she and her family entered a period of deepest mourning.

Albert dies

Prince Albert had been ill for several days but the Queen knew something was terribly wrong when he was wandering, restless, from room to room in the middle of the night. He had developed the signs of what was deemed to be typhoid fever. Victoria was extremely anxious. The doctor, Sir James Clark, said he was 'hopeful', but it was too late. Albert deteriorated rapidly. He died on 14 December 1861, aged 42, leaving the Queen in a state of shock.

'My life as a happy one is ended', wrote the grief-stricken Queen as she and her family entered a period of deepest mourning. She wrote letters on black-edged notepaper and sealed them with black wax. She replaced her colourful dresses with an entirely black wardrobe and the court wore mourning dress on all social occasions until the end of the next year. She distributed commemorative bracelets, brooches and rings containing Albert's portrait among her ladies and the bust of Albert by William Theed would feature repeatedly in family photographs. Victoria refused to appear in public, feeling unable to face her official duties without Albert. Criticism mounted as she resisted pressure from her ministers to attend public events such as the State Opening of Parliament. Discontent about her absence fuelled republican ideas, which gained popularity as the Queen's seclusion continued into the 1870s.

Above: Mourning ring with microphotograph of Prince Albert, made for Queen Victoria, c1861.

Left: The Mourning Room includes a display of Queen Victoria's earliest surviving mourning garments, and those of her two youngest children, Prince Leopold and Princess Beatrice.

The Queen's Diamond Jubilee

After many years of self-imposed isolation while Victoria mourned the loss of her 'angel', her golden and diamond jubilees returned her firmly to public life. Many statues of Victoria were commissioned for the Golden Jubilee celebrations in 1887, including one for Kensington Gardens by her daughter Princess Louise, who lived at Kensington Palace (see pages 11 and 47). The Diamond Jubilee celebrations in 1897 were an even more spectacular success. For the procession, the Queen appeared in an open landau that travelled through the streets of London towards St Paul's Cathedral. The city was heavily decorated with homemade bunting, triumphal arches and illuminations. There were deafening cheers from vast crowds of onlookers who sang 'God Save the Queen' as she passed. This enormous outpouring of adulation moved the Queen to tears.

The strong interest in music, the theatre and painting that Victoria developed during her childhood at Kensington Palace remained with her for the rest of her life. Music written by Prince Albert, etchings that they made of their children and mementoes from her early years are testament to the value that she continually placed on her close family relationships.

Queen Victoria's Diamond Jubilee portrait by W & D Downey. This photograph was actually taken in 1893, on the occasion of the wedding of the future King George V and Queen Mary, but was used as the official portrait for Victoria's 1897 Diamond Jubilee.

When Victoria met Albert

IN 1836...

PRINCESS VICTORIA WAS ONLY SIXTEEN WHEN HER RELATIONS STARTED TO FIND HER A HUSBAND

VICTORIA'S UNCLE KING LEOPOLD OF THE BELGIANS WANTED HER TO MARRY HIS NEPHEW PRINCE ALBERT

A VISIT WAS ARRANGED...

VICTORIA FIRST CAUGHT SIGHT OF ALBERT AND HIS BROTHER ERNEST WHEN THEY ARRIVED AT KENSINGTON PALACE ON 18TH MAY, 1836, ACCOMPANIED BY THEIR FATHER ERNEST, DUKE OF SAXE-COBURG-GOTHA

VICTORIA WAS DELIGHTED WHEN HER UNCLE PRESENTED HER WITH A TAME PARROT

Albert, who is just as tall as Ernest but stouter, is extremely handsome; his hair is about the same as mine; his eyes large and blue, and he has a beautiful nose and a very sweet mouth with fine teeth.

I like my Cousins extremely, they are so kind, so good, and so merry...

I sat between my dear Cousins on the sofa and we looked at drawings. They both draw well, particularly Albert.

VICTORIA'S MOTHER THE DUCHESS OF KENT GAVE A BALL AT KENSINGTON
AND ALBERT AND VICTORIA DANCED UNTIL THREE IN THE MORNING

THE NEXT DAY

ON FRIDAY 10TH JUNE, VICTORIA SAID GOODBYE TO HER FAMILY

I embraced both my dearest Cousins most warmly, as also my dear Uncle. I cried bitterly, very bitterly

Allow me, then, my dearest Uncle, to tell you how delighted I am with him, and how much I like him in every way. He possesses every quality that could be desired to render me perfectly happy.

Victoria

VICTORIA AND ALBERT EXCHANGED LETTERS OVER THE NEXT FEW YEARS, DURING WHICH TIME VICTORIA WAS CROWNED QUEEN. WHEN THEY MET AGAIN IN 1839, VICTORIA HAD TO TAKE THE INITIATIVE AND PROPOSE, AS SHE FEARED THAT ALBERT WOULD NEVER DARE NOW THAT SHE WAS QUEEN. SHE AND ALBERT HAD NINE CHILDREN AND LIVED HAPPILY TOGETHER UNTIL HIS DEATH FROM TYPHOID IN 1861. VICTORIA WAS HEARTBROKEN AND MOURNED HIM UNTIL HER DEATH IN 1901.

Left: Peter the Wild Boy (detail) by John Simon, c1726-1842.

Below: William, Duke of Gloucester (detail) from the studio of Godfrey Kneller, c1699.

Wild & boys

Growing up at Kensington Palace

Edward VIII (1936) called it the 'aunt heap' but many children, including a feral child and a future queen have spent time growing up at Kensington Palace.

'Peter the Wild Boy' caused a sensation when he arrived at the court of George I on 7 April 1726. A feral child who had been captured in the woods near Hanover, Germany, Peter was a court curiosity. He walked on all fours like a chimp, had an irrepressible laugh, spoke no language and had dark, bushy hair. A few days after his arrival, Peter was taken to Kensington to sit for William Kent's staircase painting. He was depicted holding an oak leaf and acorns – reminders of his life in the German forest. Unhindered by court etiquette, Peter would sit wherever and whenever he wished, 'before anyone, without distinction of persons'. He learned to say his own name and was given fine clothes to wear. Despite attempts to 'civilise' him, Peter's peals of laughter would ring through the palace and he was happy to find nuts or fruit when he picked people's pockets.

William Henry, Duke of Gloucester, was the future Queen Anne's only child to survive infancy. Nearby Campden House, the sickly Duke's home, afforded him regular visits to the palace, where his childless aunt and uncle, William III and Mary II, lavished gifts on him. They gave him a box of ivory carpenters' tools when renovations at the palace took his interest. He drilled his boy troops, with their wooden swords and muskets, for the King and Queen in Kensington Gardens. Mary relished his visits to Kensington when the King was away on campaign. She ordered a model ship for him just before she died. The young Duke and his friends would climb the ship's masts, work its guns and bombard the enemy with bags of peas. The unfortunate Duke died just a few days after his 11th birthday.

The baby Princess Victoria's father died in January 1820, leaving her to grow up at Kensington alone with her mother, the Duchess of Kent. It was a lonely and isolated childhood. The Princess had few friends and remained constantly under her mother's watchful eye. Days were governed by the 'Kensington System', a method of educating the Princess that the Duchess and her ambitious aide Sir John Conroy devised to prepare her for her future role and – importantly – to keep her under their control. Trips to the theatre and the opera were an escape from Victoria's solitary existence. She recorded her idols' performances in her sketchbooks and journals in the minutest detail. The Duchess and Conroy's attempts to control the Princess reached tipping point during a visit to Ramsgate in 1835. When they tried to force her to agree that the Duchess would enjoy an extended regency if the King died before she turned 18, the iron-willed Princess resisted.

good girls

Below: *Princess Victoria* (detail) after Sir George Hayter, 1866-70.

Tour 4
Modern royals

The State Apartments of Kensington Palace were first opened to the public in 1899 but beyond the closed doors, Kensington in the 20th century played a very different role as home to some of the most colourful and stylish members of the Royal Family.

At the start of the 20th century a Victorian air reigned at Kensington Palace as the private apartments were filled with many elderly ladies descended from Queen Victoria. These included two of her daughters: princesses Louise and Beatrice. Louise had been granted an apartment on the South Front of the palace, at the time of her marriage in 1873 and continued to live there until her death in 1939. Victoria was delighted that one of her daughters had moved to her old home and wrote to Louise, 'I am happy to think one of my daughters shd. live in a part of it'. Louise, an artistic, spirited and unconventional princess, who moved in bohemian circles, was never afraid of shocking her mother. A strong supporter of the feminist movement, she

privately visited the female doctor, Elizabeth Garrett, at a time when all doctors were men, and corresponded with the social reformer Josephine Butler. She was responsible for the sculpture of Queen Victoria that still stands outside the East Front of the palace (see page 11). In 1927 the fiancée of Louise's nephew, Janet Aitken Kidd, visited the Princess and found 'an utterly charming old lady dressed in Victorian clothes with a high lace collar'. When war broke out in September 1939 the redoubtable Louise refused to leave the palace but in her old age she had become increasingly frail and died in her apartment on 2 December 1939.

Louise's sister Beatrice, Victoria's youngest daughter, moved to Kensington with her children after the death of her mother in 1901. They lived in the apartments where Victoria had grown up on the east side of the palace. Beatrice spent much of her time at Kensington working on the Herculean task of sorting out her mother's papers and journals, a job she did while putting up with the thousands of footsteps from visitors walking round the grand rooms above her own home. At the start of the Second World War Beatrice left the palace to stay with friends outside London; her death in October 1944, before the end of the war, meant that she never returned to Kensington.

Left and below left: Princess Louise's apartment at Kensington, which was later refurbished for Princess Margaret and Lord Snowdon.

Right: Princess Louise made this terracotta bust of herself in the 1870s.

Opposite: Princess Louise photographed in Venice in c1890.

Many of Victoria's grandchildren also lived at Kensington, including the Countess of Athlone, Princess Alice. When she died in 1981, aged 98, Princess Alice was Queen Victoria's last surviving grandchild but had moved to Kensington with her husband, Prince Alexander of Teck, in 1923. Lively and independent to the last, Princess Alice would regularly catch the number 9 bus down Kensington High Street to visit her friend, the flower seller Ada Shakespeare. At her death it was found that nothing had been modernised or changed in her apartment since before the Second World War. The Dowager Duchess of Milford Haven was another granddaughter of Victoria and a formidable Kensington personality. In the 1930s her young grandson Philip would often stay with the Dowager Duchess during school holidays (although he had to be told not to blow his trumpet too loudly for fear of disturbing his elderly aunts). The same Philip was to leave from Kensington Palace for his marriage to Princess Elizabeth (later Queen) in November 1947. His best man was his cousin, the Marquis of Milford Haven, with whom he enjoyed an early morning gin and tonic to steady his nerves.

The years after the Second World War signalled a change in Kensington's residents, with a new generation bringing a fresher, more dynamic presence to the palace. Princess Marina, the stylish Duchess of Kent, moved in with her three children. She was a noted hostess and would hold dinner parties for her wide circle of friends, from the film star Douglas Fairbanks to the playwright Noel Coward, though she was also quite happy to go around Kensington Gardens incognito.

Shortly after their marriage in 1960, Princess Margaret and her husband, the fashionable photographer, Antony Armstrong-Jones (Lord Snowdon) came to live at Kensington. Their elegant but informal, bohemian lifestyle was quite different from most royal couples, and they transformed their large apartment on the South Front of the palace. Together they created a modern home, getting rid of the gloom and gas lamps, which were the legacy of Princess Louise, the apartment's last inhabitant. Many of the new details were designed by Lord Snowdon himself, including the efficient, striking contemporary kitchen with its unusual industrial-style cooker hood, and the theatrically grand entrance hall, entirely suitable for a nephew of the celebrated theatre designer Oliver Messel. Their home became the setting of glamorous parties for Margaret and Snowdon's friends from the world of art and show business: the actor Peter Sellers and his Swedish wife Britt Ekland, the comedian Spike Milligan, the dancers Rudolph Nureyev and Margot Fonteyn and the actress Elizabeth Taylor. Margaret, a natural hostess, cigarette in hand, would often encourage her guests to join her in after dinner renditions of songs from her favourite musicals while she played on a baby grand piano.

Princess Marina, Duchess of Kent by Dorothy Wilding, 1934.

Their home became the setting of glamorous parties for Margaret and Snowdon's friends from the world of art and show business.

Above left: The Duke of Edinburgh leaving Kensington Palace for his wedding to Princess Elizabeth at Westminster Abbey, 20 November 1947.

Above: *Princess Alice, Countess of Athlone* by Madame Yevonde, 1963.

Left: Princess Margaret, Lord Snowdon and their children, photographed at Kensington Palace in 1965.

The elegant entrance hall, which had been bombed during the Second World War, was restored to something of its 18th-century glory, under the watchful eye of the Prince.

In 1982 the residents of Kensington Palace were joined by The Queen's eldest son and his wife, the new Prince and Princess of Wales. Their new home, on the north side of the palace, was finished only a month before Diana gave birth to her first child, Prince William on 21 June 1982. Prince William was soon joined by his brother Prince Harry in 1984.

From the start, the apartment reflected the tastes of the couple. The elegant entrance hall, which had been bombed during the Second World War, was restored to something of its 18th-century glory, under the watchful eye of the Prince, with his strong interest in historic architecture. Diana's sitting room, like much of the rest of the house, was decorated in light airy colours with cosy reminders of the Princess's childhood, like her school tuck box.

The palace witnessed Diana's transformation from a shy and modest young woman to a stylish princess and hands-on mother. The Princess would often take her sons for walks in Kensington Gardens, and later see them off to their nearby prep school. An elegant woman with an interest in fashion and a need to look smart, fashion designers including the Emanuels, Bruce Oldfield and Catherine Walker would often visit Diana at home, discussing ideas for outfits and planning wardrobes for official engagements.

After the announcement of the Wales's separation in 1992 Diana continued to live at Kensington, while Charles moved to Clarence House and retained the Wales's Gloucestershire home of Highgrove. It was in her apartments at Kensington that Diana's famously candid interview with journalist Martin Bashir was filmed in 1995 and from this home that she planned the spectacular Christie's sale of 79 of her evening dresses that was held in New York, just months before her tragic death in 1997. The thousands of bouquets, cards and messages of sympathy and sadness that were left at the palace gates following the terrible news of her death remain, for many, one of the most vivid images of Kensington (see page 57).

Today, Kensington remains a royal home and residents include the Duke and Duchess of Gloucester and Prince and Princess Michael of Kent. In 2011, only months after their wedding, which was watched across the globe, the Duke and Duchess of Cambridge began using Kensington as their London home. The intense fascination about and warm affection for the couple will no doubt ensure that Kensington will continue to be a place of interest and appeal for many years to come.

The Duke and Duchess of Cambridge in 2011.

Dressed to impress

The Royal Ceremonial Dress Collection

Spectacle, splendour, exquisite needlework and sumptuous fabric can all be found in this unique collection of British ceremonial dress.

A majestic red velvet coronation robe, a delicate feather fan and a bold checked golfing suit may appear to have little in common but all are items of clothing in the Royal Ceremonial Dress Collection, cared for by Historic Royal Palaces.

This unique assembly of over 10,000 objects reveals the magnificent and complex world of dress worn at court and by members of the Royal Family. Intriguing, impressive and sometimes unexpected items in the collection offer a distinct perspective on four hundred years of royal British history. While most of the objects in the collection are owned by Historic Royal Palaces there are significant loans from the Royal Collection, Princess Margaret's family, owners of dresses worn by Princess Diana, and the Bowden Collection of Court Uniform.

Top: Plumed cocked hat, 1908, worn as part of the ceremonial uniform for the Deputy Lieutenant of Counties, Scotland.

Above: Edward VII's baby shoes, 1841. Queen Victoria kept shoes belonging to all of her nine children.

Opposite: Gold-embroidered court coat, full dress second-class uniform, made for Lord Boston in 1885.

Dress plays a crucial role in the spectacle and splendour of monarchy and the collection contains some of the grandest royal clothing ever produced from the great robes of ermine and velvet worn by kings and queens for the coronation ceremony to sumptuously embroidered dresses of satin and brocade for state dinners and weddings. Yet items in the collection also reveal a very intimate, personal side of royal dress; from clothing worn by royal children like a robust sailor suit belonging to the children of King Edward VII (1901-10) and Queen Alexandra to some of the oldest royal items in the collection: a pair of vivid green stockings and a slender knitted red shirt associated with William III. The stockings have a little 'W' worked into the upper edge and the shirt's tiny size emphasises the King's diminutive stature. The collection contains many surprises too: a series of jaunty suits worn by the fashion conscious, clothes-loving Duke of Windsor and a small silk cone of confetti rice embellished with gold letters from the wedding of Princess Victoria Eugenie, one of Queen Victoria's granddaughters, to King Alfonso XIII of Spain.

Many items in the collection were created for grand state ceremonies such as coronations and the State Opening of Parliament. The clothing worn for these occasions, often little different from the medieval and Tudor dress from which they developed, emphasise the tradition and pageantry of the ceremony. They include the coronets and robes worn by members of the peerage, with their ancient symbols instantly signalling to those in the know the position and rank of the wearer. For example: a duke's coronet is decorated with eight silver-gilt strawberry leaves and his robe has a collar with four rows of ermine, while the lesser ranked baron has a

Left: Detail of a richly-embroidered waistcoat from a court suit, 1850s.

Opposite: The 'Spitalfields mantua' (detail), 1750-5. This stunning dress of brocaded silk was made in the famous Spitalfields area of east London.

coronet with six spheres (or 'pearls') and his collar has only two rows of ermine. The richly coloured and heavily embroidered heralds' tabards are another eye-catching example of ceremonial dress represented in the collection. This ancient royal office, which originally issued pronouncements from the monarch and even today is responsible for organising state ceremonies, has a uniform decorated in metal threads with the royal coat of arms and offers a potent symbol of the pedigree and longevity of royal service.

Another key part of the collection is clothing worn on formal occasions to meet the monarch, illustrating all of the complexity and richness of court dress. Whether for a King's Drawing Room in the 18th century or the presentation of debutantes (young aristocratic girls coming out into society) to the queen in the 19th century, court dress was full of significance, shaped by tradition and governed by a strict set of rules. Until the Second World War for example, women attending court had to wear long trains, a headdress of white tulle and plumed feathers, an elbow-length pair of white gloves and carry a fan. Men's clothing was equally resplendent: dark, tailored suits worn with knee breeches and often decorated with intricate metal thread embroidery. The collection contains exquisite and opulent examples of these necessities of court dress, including feathery fans and silken shoes. However, rather than being fashionable, court dress sat outside prevailing trends; instead it was all about opulence, wealth and position, as the costly metal thread fabrics of 18th-century mantuas (formal, wide skirted dresses) and court suits in the collection clearly show. Trimmings, embellishment and embroidery were often employed to provide a dazzlingly rich effect. The creation of such magnificent clothing required both skilled workmanship and the use of expensive materials. The collection includes

many examples of the fabrics, threads and other materials needed in their production, from reels of metal thread and shimmering foils to intricate paper patterns for dense embroidery on the ceremonial uniforms worn by ambassadors and members of the royal household.

As with most dress collections the fragile nature of the objects means that they cannot be continuously displayed; but many items regularly take pride of place in exhibitions and displays at Kensington Palace. The dress in the collection is complemented by design drawings, sketches, receipts, prints and fabric, all of which help to make this a rare and rich resource to illuminate the complex, curious world of royal and ceremonial dress.

Detail of a mohair suit worn by the Duke of Windsor, 1941. The jacket is decorated with Royal Yacht Squadron buttons.

Mary II, Queen Anne, George II and Prince Augustus, Duke of Sussex all ended their days at Kensington Palace.

When royalty dies we are reminded that Death is the great leveller.

Kensington in tears

Life may have been easier in some ways for the royals of centuries past but deaths were a public, sometimes humiliating and painful affair.

William III and Mary II were the first monarchs to live – and die – at Kensington Palace. In December 1694 Mary noticed the beginnings of smallpox on her skin, calmly sorted through her papers and then told her household. William was beside himself with grief and camped by her bed until her death on 28 December. In tears he declared that 'From being the happiest, he was now going to be the miserablest creature on earth'. William lived a further eight years, ruling alone. He loved to ride his horses and while enjoying that pursuit at Hampton Court his horse tripped and he fell. He lived a few days longer but died at Kensington on 8 March 1702 leaving the crown to his sister-in-law Anne.

Queen Anne had her share of sorrows. She had a multitude of pregnancies (17) but only one child, William Henry, lived beyond the age of 2 – and he was a sickly child and died at the age of 11. Her beloved husband, Prince George of Denmark died at Kensington on 28 October 1708, making the palace so abhorrent to the mourning Queen that she kept away for 18 months after his death. As Queen Victoria was later famous for, Anne remained in isolation for months and kept George's rooms as he had left them. Anne's own death was an inglorious end to a dynasty. In the final days of her life she could only say 'yes' or 'no' and could not even sign her will. She suffered from gout throughout her life and her death was a drawn out struggle full of indignities. Her doctors bled her, blistered her, shaved her head and covered her feet in garlic in front of the members of the court who attended on her. She died at Kensington Palace on 1 August 1714 at the age of 49.

George II and his wife Queen Caroline used Kensington as their main residence and it became the focus of court life. They were the last monarchs to do so. George II suffered an ignominious end to his reign. On 25 October 1760, during his morning ablutions in the toilet, the King's valet heard a crash and found the monarch on the floor. His heart had burst! He was pronounced dead before his relatives could be summoned and was buried beside his wife in Westminster Abbey. Touchingly, the boards between their two coffins were removed so they could lie next to each other.

In later years Kensington became the focus of national and international mourning. George III's popular son Prince Augustus, Duke of Sussex, lived at Kensington for many years. His death in 1843 caused huge scenes of public condolence. The palace was opened to mourners and over 25,000 people visited to pay their respects in a single day. A special wooden staircase was built from a second-floor window to ease the flow of visitors. The Duke was buried in daylight – the first time for a member of the Royal Family – and not in a royal cemetery but in the newly built Kensal Green Cemetery.

Most famously, in 1997, the death of Princess Diana triggered an astonishing response. For two weeks members of the public filed through the palace to sign condolence books and for the first week Kensington Palace stayed open 24 hours a day to cope with the vast numbers of visitors.

An estimated 140,000 people wrote messages expressing their grief.

Princess Margaret lived at Kensington for over forty years and after her death in hospital in February 2002 her coffin lay covered in her standard at the palace before being removed at night to Marlborough House. Candles were placed in the windows of Kensington and residents and workers watched as she left the palace for the last time.

Above: One of the most iconic images of the 20th century a sea of floral tributes outside Kensington Palace following the death of Princess Diana in 1997.

Below: Among those attending the Duke of Sussex's coffin in 1843 were his piper and his devoted Burmese page.

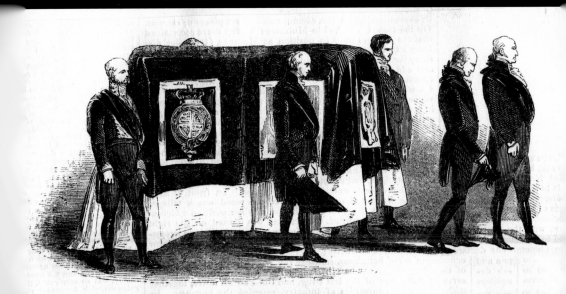

PALL BEARERS OF THE DUKE OF SUSSEX.

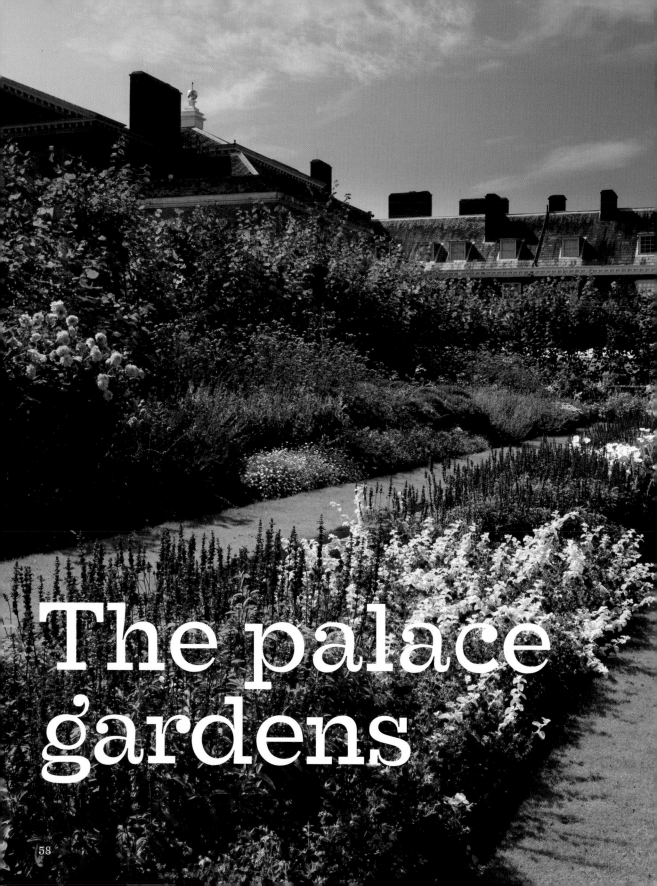

The palace gardens

Much care and expense has been lavished on Kensington's gardens by its various royal inhabitants. Some schemes were swept away as fashions changed but Queen Anne's incomparable Orangery remains. In 2012 the palace gardens were transformed, reconnecting the building with its landscape setting.

In the distant past, the wider landscape of Kensington Gardens formed a grand setting for the palace; the Round Pond is aligned on it, and echoes of the radiating avenues of trees still extend through the park.

Over time, however, this essential relationship has been lost, and only now has it been re-established with the opening up of the East Front to the Broad Walk. No great royal palace of the 17th century would be complete without its gardens, and in the 1690s the south side of the palace, where a great lawn now stretches down to Kensington High Street, was once laid out as a fine series of baroque parterres, with sinuous paths and beds, shaped dwarf trees and exotic shrubs in sophisticated arrangements (see page 7). William and Mary had spent £20,000 purchasing Nottingham House, but between 1689 and 1696 as much again was laid out improving the gardens. The South Front garden, designed by George London, possibly with the great French designer Daniel Marot, is now known only from old prints, as

it enjoyed a brief period of fashion before being swept away in the 1720s as too expensive to maintain.

Queen Anne added little to the physical fabric of the palace, except for the incomparable Orangery, but she spent large sums on the gardens, continuing the development to the north, where George London and Henry Wise had already begun to lay out a wilderness for King William in 1701. A 17th-century wilderness was far from being wild, but was a picturesque series of carefully planned winding paths and dense plantings. Anne also embellished the south gardens with fountains and an alcove containing a garden seat looking back towards the palace. This survives, but was moved to nearby Lancaster Gate in the 1860s. In 1705, 100 acres were added to the east side of the palace to form a paddock for royal deer and antelope, stretching towards Hyde Park out of which the original garden scheme was formed.

Above: During the winter months, Queen Anne's orange trees were protected from the cold inside her magnificent new Orangery. In the summer, they were transferred to the terrace outside.

Opposite: The Sunken Garden, laid out during the reign of Edward VII and opened in 1909.

The Orangery, built for Queen Anne in 1704-5.

The East Front gardens were laid out in 2012 in a new scheme inspired by the lawns, borders and topiary created by Charles Bridgeman for George II and Queen Caroline.

It is to Queen Caroline that the gardens owe much of their later development. At the end of his reign, George I had introduced exotic animals to the paddock, including tigers and civet cats and some more sedate pets in the form of tortoises and a snailery (presumably for eating). George II had these moved to the Tower of London early in his reign. His consort Queen Caroline applied considerable imagination in redesigning the wider park on a grand scale, extending the plantings and views to the far distance. The Broad Walk was laid out as a giant north-south axis, and the Round Pond (originally octagonal) was dug in 1728. The pond was set off by radiating avenues of trees, and all were aligned on the King's Drawing Room in the East Front of the palace. Further east in the park, the Serpentine was formed as a boating lake by flooding several smaller ponds. Ornamental buildings were added. These included an earth mound with a revolving summer house on top, and a fishing temple, known as the Queen's Temple, designed by William Kent and which survives to this day.

Queen Caroline by Joseph Highmore, *c*1735. The gardens at Kensington were transformed under her direction.

Another novelty was opening the gardens to the public when the Royal Family was at Richmond on Saturdays, and it became a place to be seen and show off the latest fashions.

After 1760, when the king and court no longer came to Kensington, the strict designs of the gardens began to disappear as the planting was not maintained. A sunken, terraced garden, once adorned with topiary now survives only as a slight depression to the north. The kitchen garden was kept in use for another century, providing food for the royal table from hot-houses. The site was developed in the 19th century and now lies beneath several foreign embassies in Kensington Palace Gardens.

Kensington's older landscaped gardens retain considerable charm, but most of the cluster of small gardens near the palace are more recent. The Sunken Garden is undoubtedly the most popular, with its massed bedding of flowers glimpsed between eye-catching gaps through the hedges. Created in 1909 at the instigation of Edward VII, replacing a clutter of old greenhouses and potting sheds, it was designed in the 17th-century Dutch style, laid out by the historian Ernest Law who had such influence at Hampton Court. Its covered 'cradle walk' of limes was a popular meeting place for the flocks of Kensington nannies pushing perambulators and walking their charges in the park, the real-life counterparts of the Darling children whose friend Peter Pan's spirit still clings to Kensington Gardens.

The gardens were opened to the public when the Royal Family was at Richmond on Saturdays, and became a place to be seen and show off the latest fashions.

The east and south sides of the palace were laid out in 2012 in a new garden scheme designed by Todd Longstaffe-Gowan, inspired by the old layouts of lawns, trees, borders and topiary of George II's time. The original sightlines have been restored and the palace is once again connected to its gardens and landscape setting. A small courtyard now graces the café area to the north and a serpentine walk ascends the incline towards the Sunken Garden and Orangery Gardens. Queen Victoria presides, in the form of the statue by her daughter Princess Louise, set within an octagonal basin. As throughout their history, the gardens continue to develop a green setting for the jewel of the palace.

Promenade in Kensington Gardens by John Strickland Goodall (1908-96). Kensington Gardens has always been a popular meeting place for nannies and their charges.

'A palace for

Completed in 2012, the massive project to restore and re-present Kensington Palace has absorbed staff and supporters, contractors and conservators in an ambitious scheme to open up more of the palace for our visitors to enjoy.

The key to Kensington's longevity, indeed one reason for the very survival of the palace to the present day, long after the departure of the king and court, has been the ease with which it could be adapted to new uses, and for at least part of the palace, its continuing use as a private home.

Over time, the building has suffered from fire, neglect, dry-rot and, perhaps at times, insensitive alteration. All buildings need continuing care and the most recent chapter in the story of Kensington Palace is one of repair, restoration and renewal in an ambitious project to open more of the building up, to reconnect it with its wider landscape and make it far more than a dusty museum or a place of veneration. To mark the Diamond Jubilee of Queen Elizabeth II, the palace was transformed between 2009 and 2012 with a project called 'Welcome to Kensington – a palace for everyone'. The title speaks for itself, but this was the most ambitious undertaking for perhaps a century. In the first months, swathes of vegetation that obscured views of the building and many of the high security fences were swept away to restore the 18th-century vistas and make the building prominent again in the landscape. The Broad Walk now offers a sweeping view across lawns with shaped trees on a gentle incline to a new entrance on the east side. In creating this, the original flower terrace built by Mary II was rediscovered, together with a vast network of brick culverts and drainage ditches.

Inside the palace, old storehouses and offices were emptied, and a disused courtyard roofed over with glass to create a new hub and visitor facilities, including new shops and a café. This means that visitors can now be brought into the heart of the building and ascend the King's Staircase, the Queen's Stair or the Stone Stair just as visitors coming to the palace three hundred years ago would have done. Kensington's long tradition of exhibitions also continues with new displays dedicated to presenting the best of its renowned Royal Ceremonial Dress Collection (see page 52), while several rooms now form a space for school groups and education.

The work does not end here. Much still remains to be done to improve and restore the gardens and interiors to their original splendour, and to create a venue where the stories of the people who have shaped the nation can be told. But Historic Royal Palaces, the present custodian of the palace, is committed to ensuring that Kensington Palace does the best by its rich heritage. The future continues to look bright. A new generation of royalty has come to live at the palace, drawn perhaps like their predecessors by the cosiness and informal atmosphere of the building, and so they continue a long tradition. For the millions who pass by every year, the building now stands as a beacon in the park, restored to its former glory.

everyone'
Kensington restored

Scoring brick joints in the traditional manner.

Laying new paths on the East Front.

Supporting us

Historic Royal Palaces is the independent charity that looks after the Tower of London, Hampton Court Palace, the Banqueting House, Kensington Palace and Kew Palace. Our aim is to help everyone explore the story of how monarchs and people have shaped society, in some of the greatest palaces ever built.

We receive no funding from the Government or the Crown so we depend on the support of our visitors, members, donors, volunteers and sponsors.

'Welcome to Kensington – a palace for everyone'

The transformation of Kensington Palace would not have been possible without the support of the large number of generous donors, sponsors and supporters.

The Welcome to Kensington Champions

Clarissa Baldwin
Emily Blunt
Tracy Borman
George Clarke
Beverley Cuddy
Dame Judi Dench
Juliet Gardiner
Sarah Gristwood
Adam Hart-Davis
Prof Julian Hoppit
Prof Chris Husbands
Paul Lay
Todd Longstaffe-Gowan
Sir Trevor McDonald OBE
Liza Picard
Prof Gwyn Prins
Dan Snow
David Souden
Prof Rick Trainor
Alison Weir
Kate Williams
Lucy Worsley
Sir Tony Wrigley

Our donors and supporters, most notably:

The Cadogan Charity
Mr Mark Pigott OBE
The Heritage Lottery Fund

Clore Duffield Foundation
The Weston Family

Anon
The Richard Edward Marvin Everett Trust
J Paul Getty Jnr Charitable Trust
The Gosling Foundation
The Hobson Charity
The Basil Samuel Charitable Trust
The Wolfson Foundation

The Foyle Foundation
Kevin and Penelope Lomax
Charles and Annmarie Mackay
Paulo and Caroline Pereira
Mr and Mrs Hamish Ritchie
The Rothermere Foundation
Royal Commission for the Exhibition of 1851
Peter and Esther Smedvig

and all those donors and supporters who 'Captured a Moment in Kensington Palace's Story' or joined 'Kensington's Historic Royal Family'. We are also grateful to those other donors and sponsors whose invaluable help and support has not been recorded in these pages.

Supported by **The National Lottery**®
through the Heritage Lottery Fund

heritage lottery fund

KENSINGTON PALACE IS CHANGING
I PLAYED MY PART
www.hrp.org.uk

You can still play your part in Kensington Palace's story. Please call the Development Team on **020 3166 6321** or email **development@hrp.org.uk** for more information.

Membership makes a difference

There has never been a better time to join our Historic Royal family! Membership is fantastic value for money. Membership allows you to explore and discover so much more about each of the five palaces with limitless visiting throughout the year. Your subscription also helps us continue to tell the stories and care for these amazing palaces.

To enquire about becoming a member of Historic Royal Palaces and for more information on the range of benefits you receive, please visit **www.hrp.org.uk** or call **0844 482 7788**.

Membership
makes a
difference
Join as a member today

Four more palaces to explore;
hundreds of stories to discover

Tower of London

Gaze up at the massive White Tower, tiptoe through a king's medieval bedchamber and marvel at the Crown Jewels. Meet the Yeoman Warders with bloody tales to tell; stand where famous heads rolled and prisoners wept... then discover even more surprising stories about the Tower!

Hampton Court Palace

Explore Henry VIII's magnificent palace, then stroll through the elegant baroque apartments and glorious formal gardens of William III and Mary II. Feel the heat of the vast Tudor Kitchens and the eerie chill of the Haunted Gallery, before you disappear into the fiendish Maze.

Kew Palace and Queen Charlotte's Cottage

Step into this tiny doll's house of a palace and experience the joys and sorrows of King George III and his family through a soundscape and displays of fascinating personal artefacts. Stroll to Queen Charlotte's Cottage, built in 1770, where the Royal Family enjoyed picnics and peace in a tranquil corner of Kew Gardens.

Open April – October. Entry to Kew Gardens is required to visit Kew Palace and Queen Charlotte's Cottage.

Banqueting House

Walk in the footsteps of a dazzling company of courtiers who once danced, drank and partied beneath Rubens's magnificent painted ceiling. This revolutionary building was created for court entertainments, but is probably most famous for the execution of Charles I in 1649. Spare him a thought as you gaze up at this ravishing painting – one of his last sights on earth.

We offer an exciting programme of events and exhibitions throughout the year. For more information and details on tickets and how to find us, please visit **www.hrp.org.uk**

Further reading

The Girlhood of Queen Victoria, Vols 1 and 2
Adamant Media Corporation, 2002

Royal Wedding Dresses
Nigel Arch and Joanna Marschner
Historic Royal Palaces, 2011

Diana: Fashion & Style
Beatrice Behlen and Joanna Marschner
Jarrold Publishing in association with
Historic Royal Palaces, 2007

Queen Anne: The Politics of Passion
Anne Somerset
HarperPress, 2012

The Really Useful Guide to Kings and Queens
of England
Historic Royal Palaces, 2011

Victoria Revealed: 500 facts about the Queen
and her world
Historic Royal Palaces, 2012

The Official Illustrated History of
Kensington Palace
Edward Impey
Merrell Publishers in association with
Historic Royal Palaces, 2003

William Kent: Architect, Designer, Opportunist
Timothy Mowl
Jonathan Cape, 2006

Kids' Kensington: Incredible tales from
Kensington Palace
Natasha Narayan
Historic Royal Palaces, 2012

Queen Victoria: A Biographical Companion
Helen Rappaport
ABC-CLIO Ltd, 2002

Queen Victoria's Early Letters
Edited by John Raymond
Batsford, 1963

Georgian Monarchy: Politics and Culture,
1714-1760
Hannah Smith
Cambridge University Press, 2006

William and Mary: The Heroes of the
Glorious Revolution
John Van Der Kiste
The History Press Ltd, 2008

Courtiers: The Secret History of Kensington Palace
Lucy Worsley
Faber and Faber, 2010

From Kids' Kensington: Incredible tales from
Kensington Palace

Visit our online store for our full range of books and beautiful
gifts inspired by centuries of stories from five amazing palaces:
www.historicroyalpalaces.com

Acknowledgements

Published by Historic Royal Palaces
Hampton Court Palace, Surrey, KT8 9AU

© Historic Royal Palaces, 2012

ISBN 978-1-873993-26-2

Written by Margaret Dorman, Sebastian Edwards, Alexandra Kim, Joanna Marschner, Deirdre Murphy, Lee Prosser, David Souden and Lucy Worsley.

Edited by Clare Murphy

Designed by Open Agency, www.openagency.com

Illustration for 'When Victoria met Albert' by Bill Bragg

Principal photography by Forster & Forster

Picture sourcing by Annie Heron

Abbreviations: b = bottom, c = centre, l = left, r = right, t = top

Front cover: © Historic Royal Palaces
(photograph: Forster & Forster)

Bridgeman Art Library: pages 2-3 (Private Collection), 7c (© Timothy Millett Collection), 8b (Peter Newark American Pictures), 10t (The Stapleton Collection), 12bl (The Stapleton Collection), 14t (Photo © Christie's Images), 14-15 (Private Collection), 15tr (Yale Center for British Art, Paul Mellon Collection), 29b (Private Collection), 33l (The Royal Collection © 2012 Her Majesty Queen Elizabeth II), 45 (The Royal Collection © 2012 Her Majesty Queen Elizabeth II); By permission of the British Library: page 30 (Add MS 61416 f 48r); © The Trustees of the British Museum: page 31t; Photograph by Cecil Beaton, Camera Press, London: pages 5l (detail), 11r, 49b; Copyright: Estate of Sir Hugh Casson PRA: page 50t; © English Heritage Photographic Library (from the private collection of Lord Braybrooke, on display at Audley End, Essex): page 9 (detail); Photograph by Jayne Fincher/Thefincherfiles: page 51; Getty Images: pages 49tl (Popperfoto), 57t; © Historic Royal Palaces: pages 4l, 6, 7br, 8t, 11l, 12br, 13, 16, 17t, 17b, 18t, 19, 20t, 22-3, 25b, 27b, 28t, 36b, 47l, 52, 53t (Bowden Collection), 54t, 54b, 55, 56 (iii), 58, 59r, 60t, 62, 63l, 63r, 65 (except armour: © The Board of Trustees of the Armouries), 66, 67 (illustration: Mark Beech); National Archives (PRO): pages 28-9 (background) (Works 34/1756); © National Portrait Gallery, London: pages 20b, 24-5 (detail), 25cl (detail), 25cr (detail), 31b, 44tl, 44tr, 47r, 48; © Rex Features: page 50b; By courtesy of Felix Rosenstiel's Widow & Son Ltd., London. © John Strickland Goodall: page 61; Royal Borough of Kensington and Chelsea Libraries and Arts Service: pages 7bl, 47c, 57b; The Royal Collection © 2012 Her Majesty Queen Elizabeth II: pages 4c (detail), 4r (detail), 4-5 (main image, detail), 10b, 18b, 21, 22 (detail), 26, 28b (detail), 29t, 32, 33r, 34tl, 34tr, 34b, 36c, 37, 46, 53b, 56 (i), 56 (ii), 56 (iv), 60b; Royal Horticultural Society, Lindley Library: page 59l; Teylers Museum, Haarlem, The Netherlands: page 27t; The Trustees of the Sir John Soane's Museum: page 25t; © Tate, London 2012: page 35; © Victoria and Albert Museum, London: pages 1, 5r (detail); © Yevonde Portrait Archive 49tr.

Historic Royal Palaces is a registered charity (registered no. 1068852).

www.hrp.org.uk

Find us on Facebook: Historic Royal Palaces

Follow us on **twitter** @HRP_palaces

Watch us on **You Tube**

http://www.youtube.com/HistoricRoyalPalaces

Historic Royal PALACES

Historic Royal Palaces is the independent charity that looks after the Tower of London, Hampton Court Palace, the Banqueting House, Kensington Palace and Kew Palace. We help everyone explore the story of how monarchs and people have shaped society, in some of the greatest palaces ever built.

We receive no funding from the Government or the Crown, so we depend on the support of our visitors, members, donors, volunteers and sponsors.